# **Ace** in the **Hole**

Power of Agreement: What 'A+' Leaders do differently
to generate extraordinary results

**30-Day Self-Leadership Journal**

ANNIE HYMAN PRATT

Ace in the Hole

*Power of Agreement: What 'A+' Leaders do differently*
*to generate extraordinary results*

Leading Edge Teams Self-Leadership Journal #2

www.leadingedgeteams.com



Printed in the United States of America

Cover Design: Nina Leis and Jim McGonigal

Luminare Press
442 Charnelton St.
Eugene, OR 97401
www.luminarepress.com

LCCN: 2020924539
ISBN: 978-1-64388-514-8

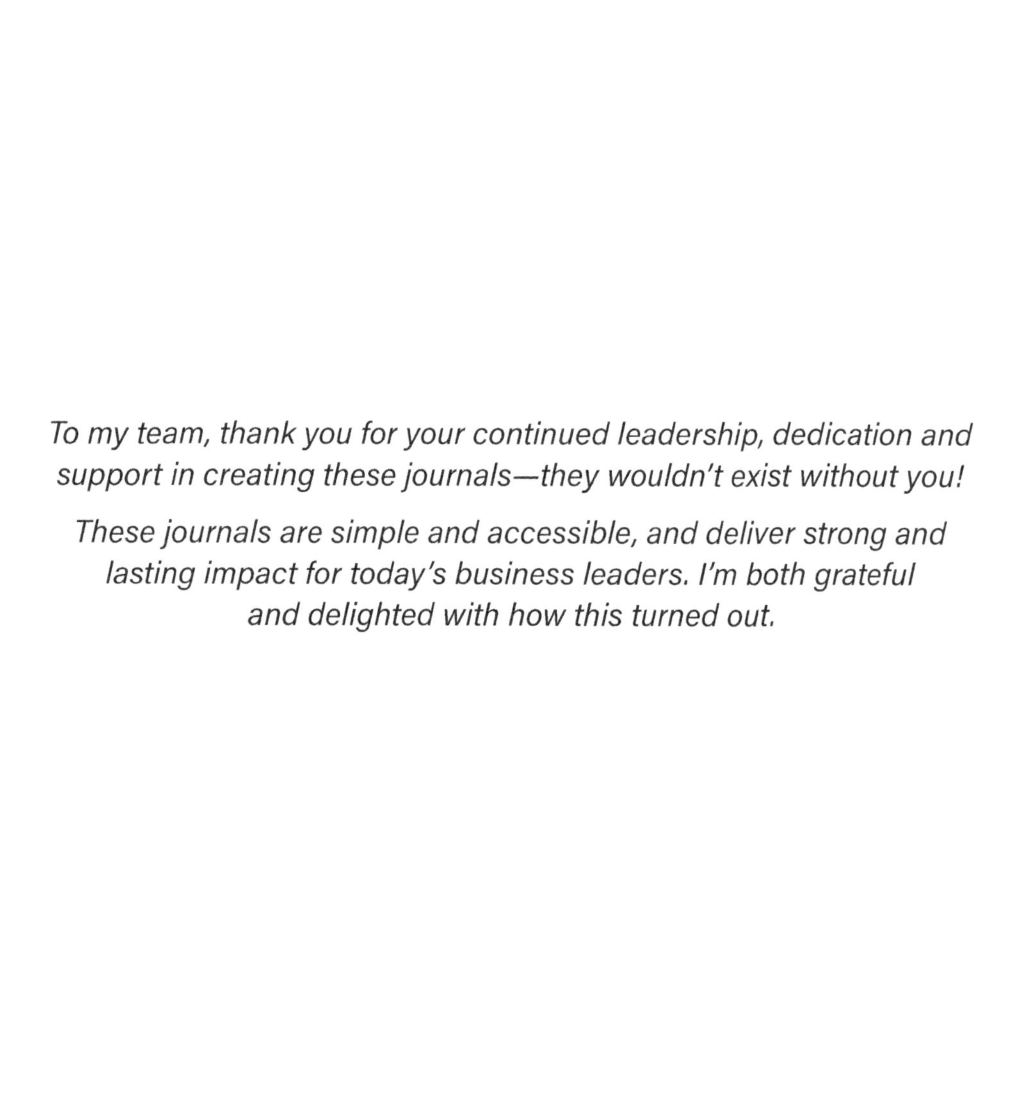

*To my team, thank you for your continued leadership, dedication and support in creating these journals—they wouldn't exist without you!*

*These journals are simple and accessible, and deliver strong and lasting impact for today's business leaders. I'm both grateful and delighted with how this turned out.*

# TABLE OF CONTENTS

# Gratitude

Thank you to all who contributed to the creation of this journal series. I especially want to thank the entrepreneurs who first requested that I develop a leadership program. Working with you and your leaders through the ups and downs of the entrepreneurial journey, has been both a challenge and a great joy.

The 'A+' Leader Development Program and Mastermind is what started me in specializing in the "people part" of business and is something I am so very proud of. It truly wouldn't have come to be without you and your support and belief in me.

Thank you to my husband David. You are an inspiring entrepreneur and the best partner I could have ever hoped for. Your support and patience has been such a gift.

To my parents Herb and Mona Hyman, thank you for your incredible example of courage in the business world and everywhere else. And to my children, thank you for being a big part of the "why" in everything I do.

# Introduction

Welcome to the second journal in Leading Edge Teams' Self-Leadership Series. My team and I are excited you have chosen our training to increase your understanding and skills for the People Part of business. We believe that learning the People Part is essential for every leader who is seeking to achieve fast and sustainable results while also wanting to avoid the overwhelm and burnout that plagues business today.

You may be continuing after completing the first journal in the series, *Ahead of the Curve: 30-Day Self-Leadership Journal.* If so, you're likely already practicing your Self-Leadership skills and are ready for more! We appreciate your continued commitment to growing your leadership and I'm sure your team does too.

Or, you may be brand new to this series—in which case, welcome! We are excited to fill you in on how you and your team can grow your People Part skills through learning to embrace Self-Leadership, to build secure relationships, and to implement conscious agreements—essential components of unified teamwork.

This journal focuses on developing your ACE agreement-making skills, which will radically change how you work with your team to unite and accomplish the company vision and goals.

The first journal (*Ahead of the Curve*) focused on learning Self-Leadership—the inner state from which individuals can engage and interact with themselves and others *without* being driven by emotional reactions and self-protection. The first journal:

1. Teaches you how self-leadership, teamwork, and human interaction work in business.
2. Teaches you the CcORE Empowerment Process (the steps to developing Self-Leadership).
3. Supports you in implementing the CcORE Empowerment Process to strengthen your leadership, increase productivity, encourage better teamwork, and reach goals effectively.

Of course, it's totally fine for you to start with this journal and learn how to utilize conscious agreement-making to transform your leadership and teamwork. However, since we will be referring to key components of Self-Leadership, just know you can dive deeper into those topics with the *Ahead of the Curve 30-Day Journal*.

Okay, so before we dive into ACE agreements, we want to explain the larger context of how business really works today and why the People Part of business has become more and more critical to business success.

## The Entrepreneur's Dilemma

After working directly with over a 100 entrepreneurs, we summarize the "entrepreneurial dream" like so: *To build a growing, profitable business that meaningfully impacts the world and allows for sustainable lifestyle freedom.*

Sounds simple enough, but to achieve all the parts simultaneously and sustainably—growth, profits, impact, and freedom—is shockingly difficult. In fact, most people don't personally know ANY entrepreneur that is truly "living the dream." Many entrepreneurs represent themselves and their companies as highly successful, and from a surface view, that very well could be the case. But when you peek behind the curtain, the vast majority of companies are filled with high levels of stress, deep systemic challenges, ongoing dysfunction, and performance that falls far short of the organization's potential.

Why is entrepreneurial business success, the kind that doesn't create large amounts of suffering, so darn elusive? Today's human beings are insanely talented at creating, organizing, and achieving goals once-thought-impossible—like space flight, cell phones, and mapping the entire human genome. So, it seems ludicrous that so few companies can successfully make money and do good in the world without sacrificing the lifestyle and well-being of the owners and the team... and yet, practically every entrepreneur today faces what we call, "The Entrepreneur's Dilemma."

Being an entrepreneur has a ton of appeal. It's exciting to grow a business, and there's nothing quite like it! You already know that it brings with it a roller-coaster of emotions, challenges, and achievements. And since you are taking the opportunity to develop and learn from our *Ace in the Hole Journal*, you most likely have already reached a certain level of success.

However, if you've been growing your business for any length of time, you also know you can't do it all by yourself. You have probably already hired some team members or are looking to bring on more. Or perhaps you've had a good sized team for a while. Either way, chances are you are still highly involved in the operations of the business, and have not been able to hand over the most important operational responsibilities. You may even be working way more since you hired team members, not less! Or you may be experiencing constant overwhelm and fear that you're headed toward burnout.

If so, you are not alone! We see the detrimental effects of the entrepreneurial dilemma all too often. Entrepreneurs come to Leading Edge Teams for support because they haven't been able to get out of the weeds and the business remains dependent on them, even as they've hired more skilled team members. These entrepreneurs are in a double bind! They want their team to take on the majority of the responsibility to operate the business, and yet they don't trust the team's ability to perform without the entrepreneur's significant involvement. Unfortunately, this lack of trust in the team's performance is usually well founded, because the team often doesn't yet have the skills or experience to reliably produce results on their own.

This is another example of the classic chicken vs. egg problem: when the entrepreneur is highly involved in work execution, the team members don't get the essential learning and experience from doing it themselves, so the entrepreneur then has to stay involved. The entrepreneur never gets enough time to do proper training because he or she is consumed with ever more responsibilities required to grow the business. Delegating some tasks may be possible, but no one else on the team can think like the entrepreneur, so at the end of the day everything crosses their desk. It doesn't take much time for an entrepreneur stuck in this cycle to feel like they have an overpaid and underperforming team—one that they have to babysit and manage while they do everything themselves!

And it gets worse, because the world now changes so incredibly fast that businesses will only survive, let alone thrive, if they're able to quickly respond. If an entrepreneur is holding all the execution and operating responsibility—which means doing all the planning, decision-making, problem-solving, resource allocation, market research, important client delivery, product development, etc.—then they can't possibly prioritize their work on the strategic changes, pivots, and innovations, that are essential for the business' medium and long-term success.

So, how do entrepreneurs avoid this trap? Many experts will say that implementing the right systems and processes is the answer; others will say you need a strong strategic plan; yet another group will say it's all about having a clear vision and concrete values. All these are certainly important, but none will have any impact on the business if you don't have the leaders and team to utilize them.

*No amount of structure, systems and processes will overcome an underperforming team!*

Breaking free of the entrepreneurs' dilemma is contingent on developing an effective and skilled team. One that is filled with 'A' Players who are high-performing and able to work with others as a united team—a team that uses ACE teamwork toward delivering the desired results. This is the only way an entrepreneur can be freed to work on the strategic and innovative parts of the business—the key to sustaining both business success and their desired lifestyle.

## The Breakthrough Paradigm Shift

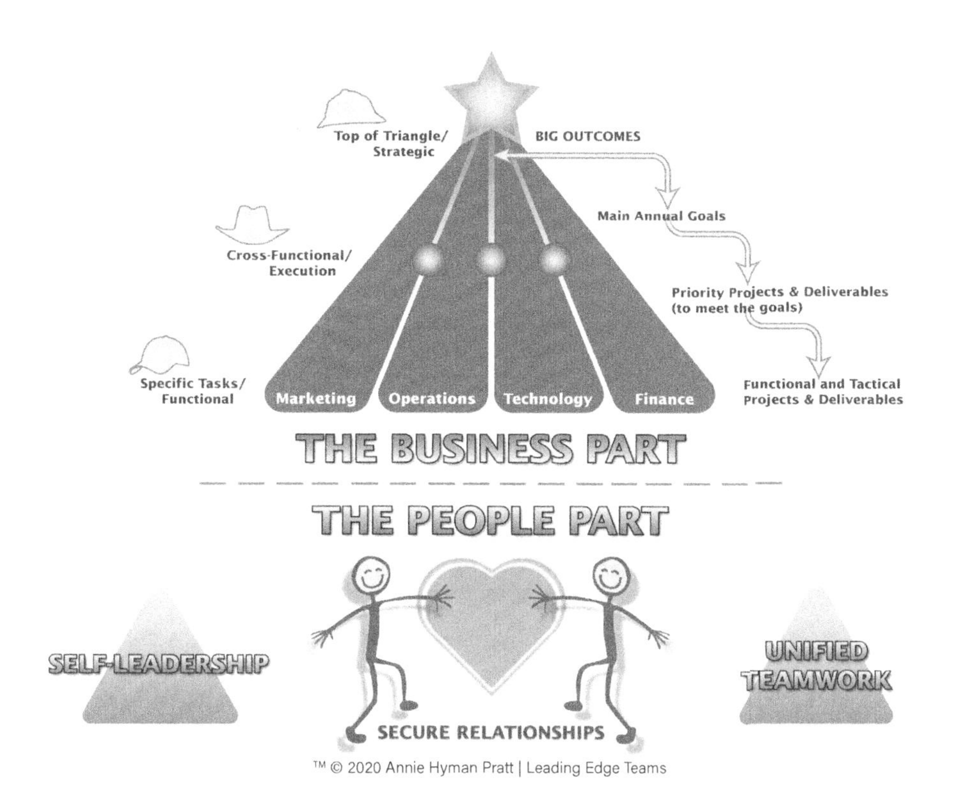



We believe that there's a fundamental reason why the vast majority of entrepreneurial businesses possess teams that perform nowhere near their potential and that are often downright dysfunctional. The reason is that businesses don't fully understand the People Part of business.

Humans are incredibly complicated beings. They have amazing thinking and creative abilities; and when they cooperate, they can achieve results that far exceed what anyone could do on their own. But one of the biggest challenges that every individual faces is working with others without being sabotaged by their automatic emotional reactivity.

When challenge or stress arises, humans are hard-wired to react as if they're under threat and they engage in "Self-Protective" behaviors. These emotionally driven behaviors are counterproductive to humans working well together.

Learning to recognize your own self-protection, and knowing what you need to do to shift out of it, sets you up to be a super powerful team player. When the whole team develops this ability to manage their emotional reactivity and show up with clear thinking, ready to collaborate—the possibilities expand exponentially.

Team members who take individual responsibility to come to the table with their best critical thinking make sure that what is driving them is not their emotions, but instead what is ultimately best for the business. This skill is critical to real world success. We have developed a process for leaders to do the inner work so that they can be the best team member they can be.

## The CcORE Empowerment Process

Listen, the bottom line is this: You have to work to master the People Part of your business, because it is a prerequisite to achieving the Business Part! This requires Self-Leadership, secure relationships, and unified ACE Teamwork.

This journal's primary focus is agreements because they are the main mechanism of teamwork. But to have good agreement-making and teamwork, all team members must participate from a place of Self-Leadership. Alright, now let me share a bit about the antidote to this pervasive self-protection: the CcORE Empowerment Process.

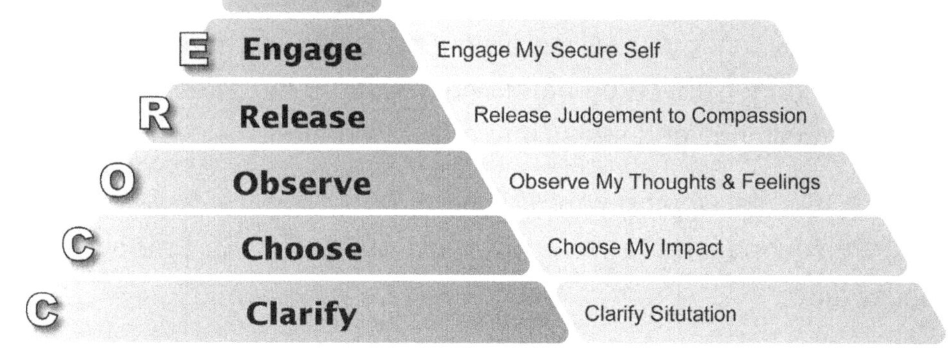


The CcORE process was developed over decades of hands-on work with entrepreneurial leaders and their teams. It helps you recognize emotional triggers and rein in self-protective, emotionally reactive behaviors.

Self-Protection is our default human hard-wiring; think of it as our "survival mode." It has a time and a place, like saving you from immediate danger, but is a tremendous hindrance when it shows up in response to perceived threats. Business is full of small challenges, but rarely those of the life-threatening variety. Instead, the challenges we face involve how we best interact together to solve problems, make important decisions, and come together to share ideas. Self-protection blocks all those genius solutions, all that good critical thinking, and all effective collaboration. That is why you need to approach these challenges differently.

The CcORE Empowerment Process, once adopted as a habit, lets you engage in your strongest critical thinking—even in the face of the most challenging business circumstances. By making it a habit, you develop strong Self-Leadership. Your self-confidence and courage to step out of your comfort zone will be evident to others, and you will more easily tap into your natural abilities and hidden talents, even under pressure.

As we mentioned earlier, in our *Ahead of the Curve Journal*, during the 30-Day journey, we focus on practicing Self-Leadership by learning how to specifically use The CcORE Empowerment Process. We highly recommend it as a powerful way to develop your Self-Leadership. Imagine the increased confidence you will feel in your decisions and agreements when you are no longer driven by emotional reaction, but when you instead transform challenge and stress into effective action.

It begins with developing your ability to first recognize Self-Protection, to PAUSE second, and to work the steps of the CcORE Empowerment Process third:

**C** **Clarify the Situation**

**c** **Choose Your Impact**

**O** **Observe Your Thoughts and Feelings**

**R** **Release Judgement to Compassion**

**E** **Engage Your Secure Self**

When you develop emotional endurance and Self-Leadership across the organization, secure working relationships are established, which means your team has the safety to step up and take risks.

Self-Leadership sets the stage for ACE teamwork, because your team becomes more open to each other's ideas, are willing to collaborate, take non-competitive actions, and build trusted relationships as they work together to achieve common goals. This is what is needed to free yourself of the double-bind that is the entrepreneurial dilemma.

Begin by practicing this today! The next time you are challenged, ask yourself, "What is the greater opportunity hidden in this challenge?" Invite your team to engage in answering this question and you will achieve the kinds of extraordinary things that brought you into business in the first place.

Download a printable version of the CcORE Empowerment Process

**https://leadingedgeteams.com/ccore-download/**

## How To Get The Most From This Journal

Again, congratulations on making the commitment to explore and improve your leadership! Over the next 30 days, you will strengthen your ability to lead and develop a team of people who achieve big business outcomes through the application of ACE Teamwork.

Applying what you learn is the best way to solidify your new approach. There are three lesson sections in this journal, each accompanied by daily practice exercises. We encourage you to do these as instructed for 30 consecutive days. If you miss a day, no worries! just get back on track the next day. Daily practice helps build your new leadership muscle and firm up your new habits.

If you have not done so already, we invite you to take our "Online Self-Leadership Quiz" to uncover your "Leadership Superpower." A link to access the quiz is provided at the end of the next section.

Finally, embrace a growth mindset as you embark on this journey! When you can see the opportunity in any challenge, you will have a distinct business advantage!

We always enjoy hearing from you. If you would like to say "Hi," share your experience, or find more team leadership tools, join our private group on Facebook. https://www.facebook.com/groups/leading.edge.teams/

***—Annie and the Leading Edge Team***

## What's Your Leadership SuperPower?

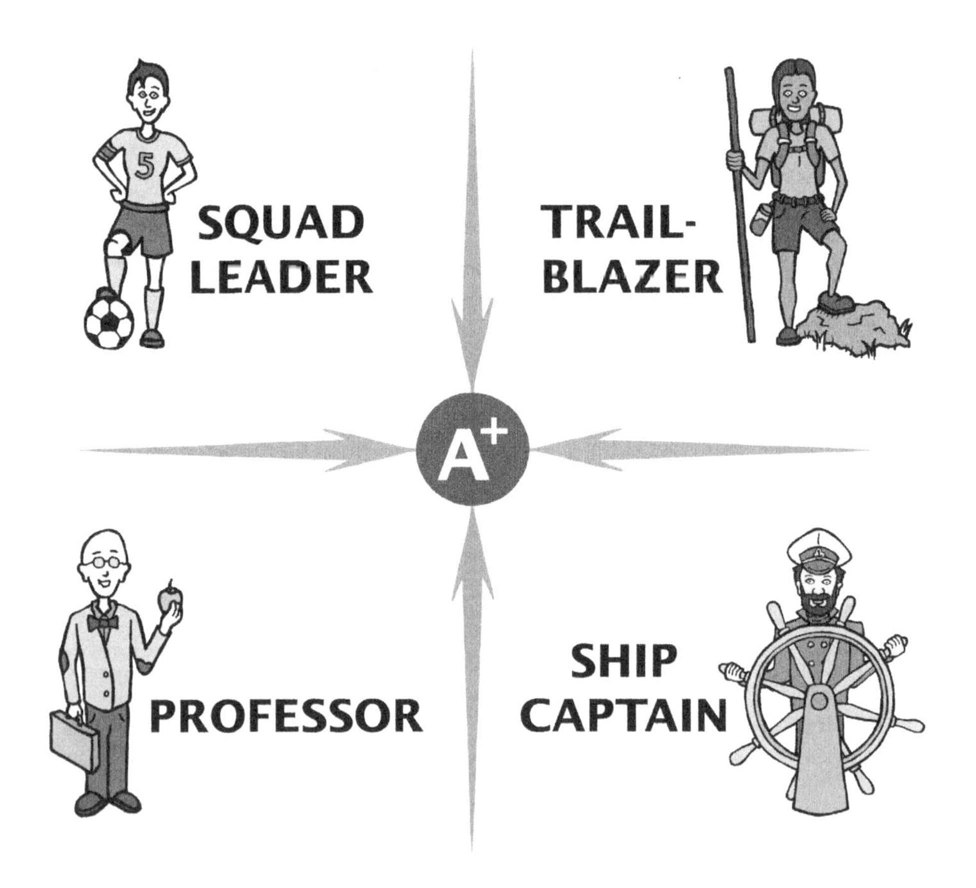

# My Self-Assessment

A successful growth journey starts with a solid assessment of where you are starting from. Only then can you recognize how far you've come at the end of the journey.

Before you jump into the first lesson, please answer the questions below to set your intentions for the next 30 days...

If you did take our Online Leadership Assessment Quiz (https:leadingedge teams.com/leadership-assessment-quiz) consider what the results revealed about your leadership superpower and blindspots. Awareness is key to making any change.

So, take a few moments to answer the questions here and....

Let the journey begin!

## Leadership Intention Questions:

▶ What do you most hope to get out of this 30-day process?

- What are your biggest challenges with teamwork or interacting with your team?

- In your ideal vision, what would be going differently in your interactions and collaboration with your team?

- What do you most need to strengthen or improve in your leadership for the year ahead?

- Which parts of your leadership hold you back from achieving greater, more effective results?

- If you haven't yet, take the Online Leadership Assessment Quiz and find out if you are a trailblazer, squad leader, professor or ship captain: [record answer below]

**https://leadingedgeteams.com/leadership-assessment-quiz**

SECTION 1

# ACE Teamwork: How Agreements Generate Business Results

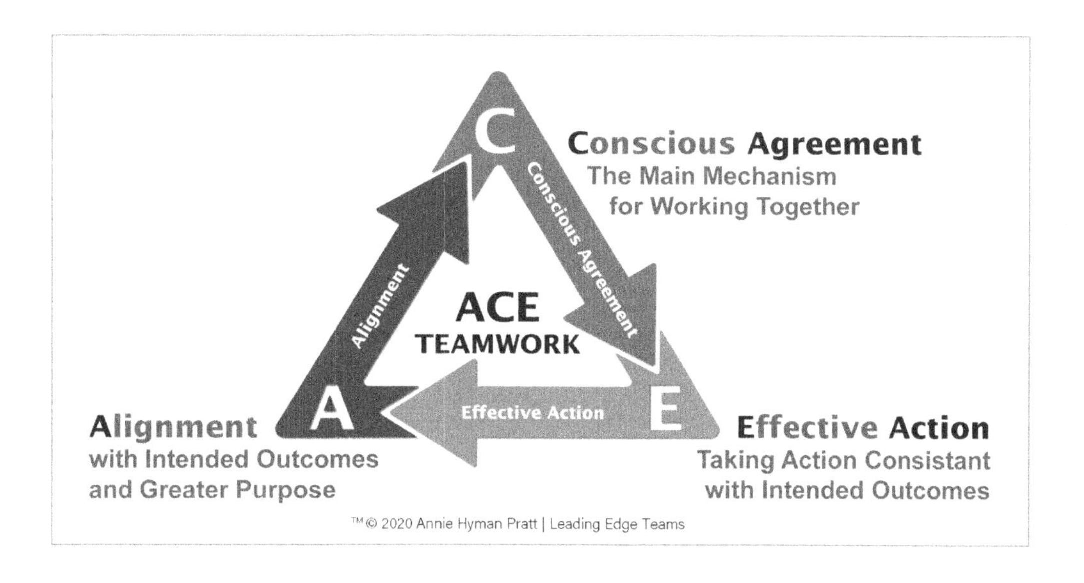

*"If you want to go fast, go alone. If you want to go far, go together."*

—AFRICAN PROVERB

# Lesson 1

Making agreements seems like such a simple undertaking. The prevailing belief is that every functional adult is capable of making good agreements. But this disregards the complexity involved. We generally define a good agreement as one where the people carry out their commitments by doing what they said they would do. We all know that it's practically impossible to work with someone who regularly breaks their commitments.

To achieve anything as a team, we need to anticipate and trust that our teammates will take the actions we expect, otherwise the game becomes chaos, whether it's in sports or business. Have you ever played a game with a child and had them add in a new rule anytime the outcome was turning out differently than they expected? You may play along to keep them happy, if that is what "winning" is for you! Or, you may get frustrated and quit the game.

*Making* and *keeping* agreements is clearly critical to humans working together productively. So, it makes sense that we harshly judge those who don't consistently keep their agreements as careless, selfish, or even disrespectful. Breaking agreements is such a social transgression in today's society that it's considered a lack of integrity or a character flaw. You've probably heard the phrase "Be true to your word" and maybe thought to yourself "Hmmm, I better be true to my word or I won't be respected."

### Agreements are a Process, Not a Promise

With this old way of thinking, your ability to make and keep agreements is directly linked with your integrity. I would like to challenge this notion by inviting you to think of them this way: *"Agreements are a process, not a promise."*

When you hear the word "agreement" you might think of "commitments" or "promises kept," but that is too narrow a definition given the complexity of business. In business, **the purpose of an agreement is to take the best coordinated set of actions to achieve a result.** Each agreement in and of itself isn't the valuable part—the value comes from what is achieved when CEOs, managers and teams utilize agreements to work together.

In business, an agreement is *not* a hard-core contract that can never be changed or a promise that can never be broken. Because circumstances are constantly changing, agreements must be changed to account for new information and developments. Agreements are meant to be made, examined, renegotiated, re-examined, dropped, modified, changed, or kept exactly as is. It all depends on the situation; an excellent agreement is either still effective, or modified to become more effective—so that it will achieve the result. That is why it bears repeating, "Agreements are a process, not a promise."

As is true with every goal, each member of your business team has to have a solid understanding of their part in helping to attain it. When your team is aiming their collective efforts strategically toward the same target, you will experience sustainable business growth and success.

### INDIVIDUAL ROLE—Every Team Member's First Company Agreement

You might be wondering, "Where do I start in creating a culture of conscious agreements?" The answer is super simple—conscious agreements start with role clarity. Clarifying exactly who does what is the first way that you and your team members align on expectations and know what successful performance looks like.

If you don't have roles clearly defined, there's a good chance that you are an entrepreneur that bounces all over, giving input, instruction, and doing tasks, at all levels of the organization. This is an all-too-common trap for founders! When you are involved in "everything," jumping around without any real structure or organization, your team becomes confused about what is expected of them.

When team members each know their role and understand how their part fits into the big picture, they are better equipped for teamwork. That is why when we have a client experiencing chaos and overwhelm, we start by clarifying what each person is doing—their job title, function/department, responsibilities, and tasks. You can do the same by identifying each of those things for yourself and for each of your team members.

**Moving from Authority and Control to Unified Team Driven Results**

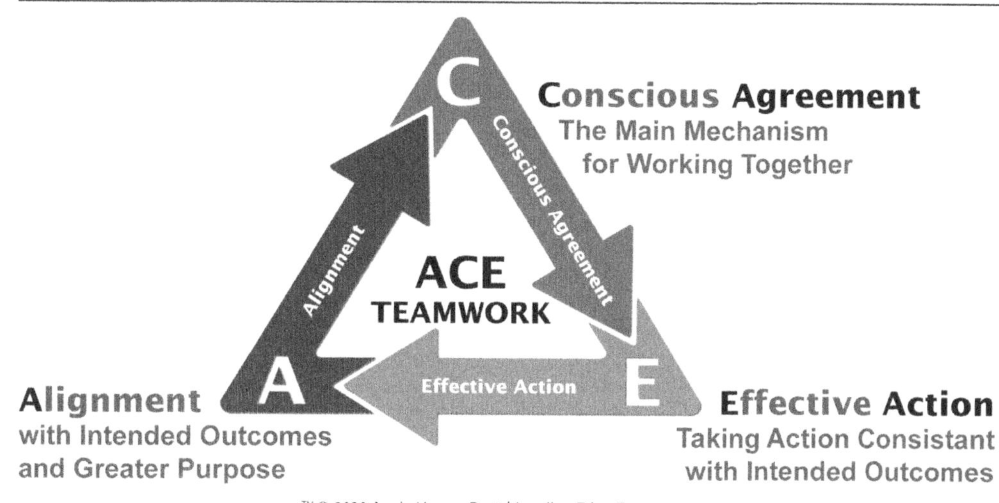


**The Highest Performing Teams Consistently Make Great Agreements**

### The ACE Agreement-Making Process

We mentioned earlier that agreements are the main mechanism allowing team members to work together toward business results. We call this ACE Teamwork, and it has three parts that join forces to achieve desired outcomes.

- **A stands for ALIGNMENT:** Seeing eye to eye on intended business outcomes and the purpose behind them
- **C stands for CONSCIOUS AGREEMENT:** Where team members think critically and negotiate responsibility to agree on the actions they will each take to generate the intended outcomes
- **E stands for EFFECTIVE ACTION:** Where team members fulfill their agreements and take action consistent with the intended outcomes

Utilizing ACE teamwork sets your people up to openly share important information and engage to make the best agreements, as you and the team steer the business together. When your team consistently makes and keeps effective agreements, you are able to let go and trust your team because they achieve consistent results. This ultimately is the only way for entrepreneurs to get themselves out of the weeds and banish burnout for good!

### The A in ACE: ALIGNMENT (to intended outcomes)

In business, all decisions, agreements and actions are meant ultimately to achieve outcomes. Because of that, alignment to those outcomes is imperative; this means having a shared understanding of what a successful outcome entails and why it matters (the bigger purpose behind the outcome). This clearly-defined, intended outcome then becomes the anchor point for the team in working together. Achieving this goal is how teams "win the game."

Without alignment, your organization **1)** won't have the foundation for good *decision-making*, **2)** will struggle to *allocate resources effectively*, and **3)** will struggle to *work as a united team* to achieve the goals.

In our experience, when people see that everybody *isn't* on the same page, all kinds of dysfunction seeps in. People often become confused and paralyzed, preferring to take no actions rather than take the wrong actions. Or they become high-driving and controlling, pursuing whatever they personally believe is most important when they don't have all the information. These dysfunctions lead to poor performance, which leads to more dysfunction—all because the team wasn't clear on the goals and couldn't align their actions with them. We can't overemphasize how imperative having clear goals is to business success.

## Clearly Defined Goals are "Smart":

**S**pecific—**M**easurable—**A**chievable—**R**elevant—**T**ime Bound*

Team members can only effectively align with goals if they know the meaningful and specific details of the desired outcome. Utilizing the acronym S.M.A.R.T. is a simple way to assess if your communication of the intended result will be effective and complete.

When a goal is too fuzzy, it will be hard for the team to get the result. The reason for this is quite obvious: when something is too general it can be interpreted numerous ways! This can lead to team members spending precious time working in opposite directions thinking they are headed to the same outcome. Or worse, they won't get started at all because they aren't clear on whether the ball is in their court.

Consider the following goal:

> *Upgrade our membership site to create raving fans who refer all their friends and family and greatly increase our revenue.*

Sounds pretty good, right? But what does success really look like here—how will the team KNOW they have achieved the goal? Consider

* S.M.A.R.T. GOALS Trademark of LEADERSHIP MANAGEMENT INTERNATIONAL, INC.

this goal instead, which has all the elements and specifics of making it S.M.A.R.T.:

> *Upgrade the membership site to greatly improve the ease of use for our customers, increasing customer retention by 30 percent, creating raving fans who actively refer clients, and double our referral rate by December 2020.*

This goal describes the results with a strong amount of specificity so that everyone working together on this goal have the same intended results in mind. Without the specificity, everyone will have their own, different definition or picture of success in mind, which becomes a big barrier to achieving the goal!

**The C in ACE: CONSCIOUS AGREEMENT-MAKING (the main mechanism of teamwork)**

In business, there are many assumed agreements, which makes sense because the activity of engaging in a negotiation to make clear and explicit agreements takes time. However, when team members don't engage in explicit, conscious agreement-making, there are often major misunderstandings and misalignment, which takes much more time, focus, and resources to solve later. By explicitly negotiating a **Conscious Agreement,** you create the space for questions, clarifications, and stronger alignment—all of which ultimately lead to better results.

Think about how you might approach an agreement to work with a colleague on a small, new project. If you're like most people, a typical interaction to make an agreement might sound something like: "I will do these tasks, while you do those tasks. This should get the project done by the deadline." With so little detail and discussion, it all seems reasonable to the other person and they easily agree. However, this type of agreement sets everyone up to fail! It seems expeditious—they certainly got to an agreement quickly—but the lack of engagement to understand all that's involved causes problems and confusion that later takes much more time to solve.

Making Conscious Agreements requires that each participant think about what other commitments, priorities and tasks he/she already has, while cooperating with other team members to address their needs and account for the greater goals of the company. What makes an agreement "conscious" is that each team member has thought through what's involved and the impacts of the agreement before they make it. By doing so, they make commitments that 1) they are confident they can actually keep and 2) that best work to achieve the outcome.

With a Conscious Agreement, each person involved clearly knows what they're expected to do and what they expect others to do. Conscious Agreements are *interdependent* with Alignment and Effective Action. Here's a simple metaphor: In your leadership toolbox, Conscious Agreements are like the screw driver (main mechanism) that drives the screw through a knob to a cabinet door (effective action) to make a kitchen cabinet easy to open and close (the goal).

**Agreements are not a matter of Integrity—They're a matter of Skill**

The greatest misunderstanding surrounding agreements is the notion that they're about "integrity" and that failing to meet the terms is a personal failing on the part of the individual. Thinking of agreements this way rides on the impossible assumption that a perfect agreement can be made, which then becomes a promise to be kept at all costs.

Seeing agreements as a "promise" leads to behaviors that are counterproductive to achieving the result. Here's the thing, if I'm highly concerned about being perceived poorly as a person who doesn't keep my promises—then I will prioritize keeping my agreements (promises) ahead of getting the intended results!

An example: Let's say you agree to be at a planning meeting today for next week's book launch signing event. But then you get unexpected news that the printer has a major problem and the books won't be ready for the event! Now you must go immediately into problem solving mode and attending a planning meeting will prevent you from doing that! So, keeping the original agreement would keep your integrity intact, but it would also be disastrous for your upcoming event! I hope this extreme example grabs your attention, because it's important to see that agreements are a process and NOT a promise. As situations change, the agreements involved may need to change as well.

Lastly, when business agreements are perceived primarily as a matter of personal integrity and making promises, people become reluctant to make any agreements at all, fearing that a situation may change and put them in a lose-lose situation. No one wants to risk that.

The real solution when an agreement can't be kept is to bring people back to the table and renegotiate, without judging each other! However, as humans it's pretty hard to not judge, especially when a situation is stressful. We've all had situations where we judged ourselves or someone else when an agreement wasn't met, which made it more difficult to renegotiate and find a new solution. That's why it's important to remember that your integrity is not at stake every time you make an agreement. Of course this doesn't mean it's ok if an employee *never* keeps their agreements. That's another story—one that may end in hiring a new employee!

### The E in ACE: EFFECTIVE ACTION

Effective action is the kind of consistent, productive action that is aligned to achieve the planned and agreed-upon intended outcome. These actions will usually be the exact ones specified in a conscious agreement, since that's the whole point of making a conscious agreement in the first place!

Agreements are how you intend to carry out your alignment, effective action is how you carry out your agreements! But, there's a catch: when things don't go according to plan, the individual team member must make a choice that's in accordance with the alignment (the big picture and intended outcome) but maybe not the agreement. Sometimes a situation changes, making an agreement no longer effective because it won't make progress toward the desired outcome. Creating robust agreements allows people to have what they need to make those kinds of decisions.

Luckily, an effective approach to crafting agreements should make the need to take actions different than agreed, a rarity. However, because change is the only constant, the best agreements always have a back-up or plan B. Business is dynamic and has a lot of moving parts, so giving your employees the tools to become "captain" once in a while is imperative. If the captain is below deck and a crew member has to guide the ship, they need to know where they're going.

**In ACE Teamwork, each team member asks, given all that I desire to achieve, and all the related context of what's happening in the current situation, am I taking the right action toward the business' intended outcome?** Because at some point, something may not go as expected: Supplies are delayed, vendors go out of business, a key player quits unexpectedly, the train is late, the client gets food poisoning, the printer dies, etc.

The point of Effective Action is that you're thinking on your feet, keeping in step with the action that's going on around you to achieve the most in the moment.

People operate according to what they believe to be agreements, expectations and commitments—whether or not they're articulated. If you haven't discussed your agreements out loud, there's a good chance that you are working with implied or assumed agreements that you may or may not know about. These hidden or unspoken agreements can cause people to take actions that are counter-productive—taking you away from where you intended to be.

Making explicit agreements, together as a team, is a conscious choice. These agreements serve as a map for everyone to navigate their part in teamwork. It's also a huge time and energy-saver, because operating without using the tool of agreements often leads to misunderstandings, conflicts, feelings of being disrespected, and other forms of division in the team—and resolving those types of issues are immensely draining and time consuming.

I hope you can hear that embracing conscious agreement-making is not only effective, but it creates a win-win culture of communication and personal responsibility too!

"When you're leading, it's not about you. However, you are an important resource to achieve the outcome and to provide support to others."

—*ANNIE HYMAN PRATT*

# Day 1

▶ What agreements did you participate in making or changing today?

▶ How did those agreements work out?

- Did you identify any implied or assumed agreements that you needed to address?

- Where might you benefit from making a more conscious, clear agreement?

- Did you make any agreements when you were under pressure or stress? If so, what were they? How did they turn out?

- Did your team make any new agreements today? Do you think they made effective agreements that they can keep?

- Did you have a win today from making a conscious agreement? What was the agreement? What was the win?

"Structure and processes are very important. In fact, there's a principle in psychology that the more structure and process you have, the less emotional things become."

*—ANNIE HYMAN PRATT*

# Day 2

▶ What agreements did you participate in making or changing today?

▶ How did those agreements work out?

- Did you identify any implied or assumed agreements that you needed to address?

- Where might you benefit from making a more conscious, clear agreement?

- Did you make any agreements when you were under pressure or stress? If so, what were they? How did they turn out?

- Did your team make any new agreements today? Do you think they made effective agreements that they can keep?

- Did you have a win today from making a conscious agreement? What was the agreement? What was the win?

"Choose your impact—show up to lead, know your role, and rely on your team's strengths."

*—ANNIE HYMAN PRATT*

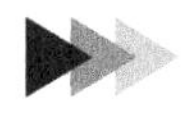

# Day 3

▶ What agreements did you participate in making or changing today?

▶ How did those agreements work out?

▶ Did you identify any implied or assumed agreements that you needed to address?

▶ Where might you benefit from making a more conscious, clear agreement?

▶ Did you make any agreements when you were under pressure or stress? If so, what were they? How did they turn out?

- Did your team make any new agreements today? Do you think they made effective agreements that they can keep?

- Did you have a win today from making a conscious agreement? What was the agreement? What was the win?

"Whenever it seems like there's an impossible problem—it's a clear sign that I have a part to play in resolving it."

—*ANNIE HYMAN PRATT*

# Day 4

▶ What agreements did you participate in making or changing today?

▶ How did those agreements work out?

- Did you identify any implied or assumed agreements that you needed to address?

- Where might you benefit from making a more conscious, clear agreement?

- Did you make any agreements when you were under pressure or stress? If so, what were they? How did they turn out?

- Did your team make any new agreements today? Do you think they made effective agreements that they can keep?

- Did you have a win today from making a conscious agreement? What was the agreement? What was the win?

"Safety does not mean being comfortable. In fact, the act of being in leadership means taking more risks. It requires courage to step up and take more ownership for delivering outcomes. That's why we need safety."

—*ANNIE HYMAN PRATT*

# Day 5

▶ What agreements did you participate in making or changing today?

▶ How did those agreements work out?

- Did you identify any implied or assumed agreements that you needed to address?

- Where might you benefit from making a more conscious, clear agreement?

- Did you make any agreements when you were under pressure or stress? If so, what were they? How did they turn out?

▶ Did your team make any new agreements today? Do you think they made effective agreements that they can keep?

▶ Did you have a win today from making a conscious agreement? What was the agreement? What was the win?

"One of the most powerful things you can do for someone else is express your belief in them."

*—ANNIE HYMAN PRATT*

# Day 6

▶ What agreements did you participate in making or changing today?

▶ How did those agreements work out?

- Did you identify any implied or assumed agreements that you needed to address?

- Where might you benefit from making a more conscious, clear agreement?

- Did you make any agreements when you were under pressure or stress? If so, what were they? How did they turn out?

- Did your team make any new agreements today? Do you think they made effective agreements that they can keep?

- Did you have a win today from making a conscious agreement? What was the agreement? What was the win?

"I think of a mindset shift as how I'm going to think differently about the thing I want to change."

*—ANNIE HYMAN PRATT*

# Day 7

▶ What agreements did you participate in making or changing today?

▶ How did those agreements work out?

- Did you identify any implied or assumed agreements that you needed to address?

- Where might you benefit from making a more conscious, clear agreement?

- Did you make any agreements when you were under pressure or stress? If so, what were they? How did they turn out?

- ▶ Did your team make any new agreements today? Do you think they made effective agreements that they can keep?

- ▶ Did you have a win today from making a conscious agreement? What was the agreement? What was the win?

"Our old way of thinking is not going to get us where we want to be in the future."

*—ANNIE HYMAN PRATT*

# Day 8

- What agreements did you participate in making or changing today?

- How did those agreements work out?

- Did you identify any implied or assumed agreements that you needed to address?

- Where might you benefit from making a more conscious, clear agreement?

- Did you make any agreements when you were under pressure or stress? If so, what were they? How did they turn out?

- Did your team make any new agreements today? Do you think they made effective agreements that they can keep?

- Did you have a win today from making a conscious agreement? What was the agreement? What was the win?

"Even in complex business circumstances, you have choice and can take actions to move your business effectively forward."

*—ANNIE HYMAN PRATT*

# Day 9

▶ What agreements did you participate in making or changing today?

▶ How did those agreements work out?

- Did you identify any implied or assumed agreements that you needed to address?

- Where might you benefit from making a more conscious, clear agreement?

- Did you make any agreements when you were under pressure or stress? If so, what were they? How did they turn out?

- Did your team make any new agreements today? Do you think they made effective agreements that they can keep?

- Did you have a win today from making a conscious agreement? What was the agreement? What was the win?

"When working with your team, a powerful phrase is:
'how are you seeing it?'"

*—ANNIE HYMAN PRATT*

# Day 10

- What agreements did you participate in making or changing today?

- How did those agreements work out?

▶ Did you identify any implied or assumed agreements that you needed to address?

▶ Where might you benefit from making a more conscious, clear agreement?

▶ Did you make any agreements when you were under pressure or stress? If so, what were they? How did they turn out?

- ▶ Did your team make any new agreements today? Do you think they made effective agreements that they can keep?

- ▶ Did you have a win today from making a conscious agreement? What was the agreement? What was the win?

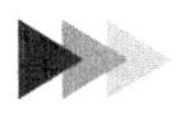

# 10-Day Check-in

*ACE Team Triangle*

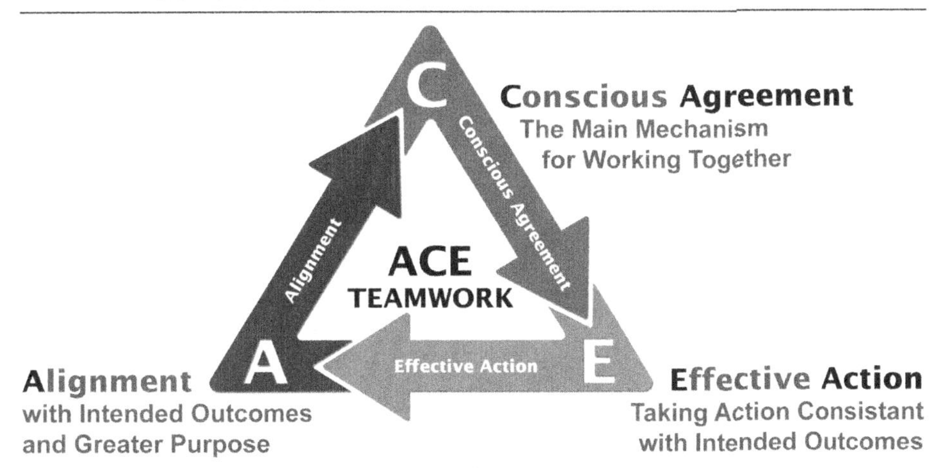

Review your answers over the past 10 days. Next, reflect on the questions below and make note of what you're noticing.

- ▶ So... How did the past ten days go for you?

- ▶ Did you notice any common themes or challenges in the past ten days?

- ▶ Where are agreements working well for you with your individual work and your teamwork?

- What would you like to do differently in your teamwork? What agreements could potentially facilitate a more positive outcome and greater business results?

Remember, the team is the engine of your business! And agreements are how you get things done!

Download a printable copy of the ACE Triangle:

**https://leadingedgeteams.com/ace-download/**

SECTION 2

# Step By Step: How To Make Effective Agreements

"Brave leaders are never silent around hard things."

*-BRENÉ BROWN*

# Lesson 2

A common blindspot in forming agreements is the expectation that you will make the perfect agreement and that it will never need to change. In business, this is just not realistic. *This is why we cannot stress enough, how it is important to create an environment of psychological safety to raise issues and renegotiate agreements.*

The truth is, as things move forward, you get new information. The external environment changes, customer expectations shift—and the plan that you made at point 'A' may no longer be the one that can deliver the desired outcome today. Because of this, all agreements are meant to be negotiated so they can be reassessed as things unfold, and renegotiated when new information arises that requires a change to reach the desired outcome.

First and foremost, agreements turn your goals into effective action. Getting results requires that each person know the answers to these questions when doing their part in a task or project:

**Basic Agreement-Making Formula**

- What are you going for? (intended outcome)
- Why? (context/purpose it serves for the company)
- How? (my part, your part)
- What if? (if things go off track, how will we recover agreement?)

Agreements align our actions so we can achieve business outcomes together. As the primary mechanism of teamwork, agreements support the team to take the kinds of action that collectively add up to successful business outcomes.

Teams that deploy ACE teamwork utilize a simple, common process to get better results. Clear agreements help team members recognize early and articulate when things are headed off track, so they can be addressed quickly and effectively. This is not only good teamwork, it's good for the bottom-line.

To negotiate solid agreements and surface issues and changes early, team members need psychological safety. It's extremely hard for humans to put themselves in a position of raising a problem or mistake when they fear being blamed or judged. So the more safety you generate, the more people will be willing to step up and take risks. Trusting they will not be perceived negatively will empower them to give it their all.

Secure relationships are ones where the trust in each other is high—that team members have each other's back—so members can drop their self protections and focus on achieving outcomes.

### Entrepreneurial Companies NEED Good Agreements

Many entrepreneurial companies operate in constant tension—running from fire to fire, never able to get ahead. To break this cycle, you actually need to slow down! This will feel like the antithesis of what you've learned to do, but it's effective, and here's why: under pressure, your team members are the most vulnerable to self-protective thinking and behaviors. This means they are being led by their emotions and their good critical thinking is not fully available—and by the way, yours probably isn't either.

Agreements made when people feel stressed or pressured often need to be remade—costing more time in the long run. This is why we say, "you need to slow down to speed up!" It is key in business to remember that there is a short term and a long term vision. If you only solve the problem for the moment, you might be undercutting the path to your brightest future. It is important to make sure you are looking at the facts, considering all angles and thinking through the best response to the challenge at hand, while also serving to move yourself forward towards your big future desired outcomes.

Good agreements also help avoid burnout. Your team is made up of humans who are a limited resource (there are only so many hours in the day!), and in entrepreneurial companies the big goals tend to stretch the available resources to their absolute limits. So many CEOs have this innocent belief that they can just keep adding things on to their people's plates. "This is a good idea, let's do both! This is also a good idea, let's do all three!" But at some point, the spaghetti piles up too high and meatballs roll off the plate. Using good agreements set the team up to use the resources (including themselves) as effectively and efficiently as possible. Remember, your team is your most valuable resource and should be preserved and treated as such!

### DELEGATION—Agreement Script

Delegation is one of the most common types of agreement made in business. A delegation is simply a situation where one person is requesting another person to take a NEW responsibility to achieve an outcome.

The number one trap of delegation (and in making all agreements) is delegating *tasks*. Directing someone to do a set of tasks puts them in an extremely weak position to achieve a result because 1) they don't know the desired result or the important context of why it matters, 2) they can only do exactly what you tell them since they have no other information, and 3) they can't do any problem solving, or even recognize if they have a problem, so they have to keep coming back to you for help.

**The solution is to delegate outcomes!** As the delegator, make sure you clearly define success. Giving context for the overall picture is also important so that the person taking on the responsibility understands how their part relates to the whole—the purpose of the project in the first place—*and the all-important whole outcome.* What outcome are you delegating? What does it look like when it's completed successfully?

Remember, *every agreement, including delegation, is a two-way responsibility.* You play a part in achieving the result, even if you are shifting the major responsibility to another person. Your role will likely become more about supporting the other person to achieve the result than actually doing the work. This is a critical role in teamwork.

**Delegating Outcomes**

An example of just delegating tasks might sound like this, "I need you to write an email that communicates the new schedule to all the event participants. Here's the timeline of the events."

This might seem pretty clear and simple on the surface, but when you imagine yourself doing the task, you immediately see that you're missing key information! Here are some questions that likely need answering for the team member to actually achieve the result that the delegator has in mind.

- What is the bigger context here—are the participants receiving a packet of information and this is just a reminder? Or is this the only notice of the schedule they'll receive prior to the event?
- Why do the participants need the "new" schedule—did the schedule change? Did they get a different schedule before or is this the first time they're seeing the schedule?
- Will this be part of an email series? Or, are they expecting this because you mentioned you'd send information to them?
- Is there any other information that needs to be included in this email? Any graphics or logos?
- When is the event? When does this need to go out?
- What happens if it doesn't go out on time?
- Do you want to review the email before I send it?

- I have six other emails to write in the next two days—how much of a priority is this?
- Will you talk with the designer if it needs graphics? I know she is overloaded with work right now.
- Should I text you if I have questions or challenges? Or should we meet tomorrow morning?

As you can see in this example, the recipient of this task would have no idea what this is really all about, why it matters and how it's meant to turn out. The recipient couldn't do the critical thinking required to avoid mistakes or make things more efficient even if they wanted to! And ultimately, their chance of producing the intended result is unlikely.

Here is the simple formula to delegate the right way:

**Delegation Script—6 Steps**

1. The intended outcome looks like:
2. The purpose and benefits are:
3. How will you (the recipient performing work) approach this and what do you need to be successful?
4. What challenges might you encounter? How will you (we) respond to those?
5. How will you (we) monitor and/or follow up on progress? How will you (we) respond to significant challenges and urgent issues?
6. How will I know when the work is complete and the result has been achieved?

Below we cover each step in depth, and we also include how we'd take our example above and do it the right way.

### 1. The intended outcome looks like ________________________

- **The "WHAT"**
- Important information that defines the successful outcome.

This includes:

- Details such as how the outcome will look, sound, feel, taste, and smell.
- The level of quality and/or quantity.
- Deadlines, timelines and milestones.
- Other success criteria defined by the company.

***Example:*** *I'd like you to write an email to update the participants of our upcoming event. Some of the speakers couldn't make their original times. Here's the new timeline of the speaker sessions. The email needs to catch people's attention and motivate them to read it! It is also important to include a link to the membership portal, so that the participants can update their selections there. We want to send out the email before noon tomorrow.*

**2. The purpose and benefits are ______________________**

- **The "WHY"**
- Related context, why achieving the outcome is important (i.e. the greater purpose served by achieving the outcome).
- Often includes what the outcome will provide, enable, or make possible—for example, achieving the defined outcome may provide more capacity, ability, time, leverage, etc.

The delegation recipient needs this context so that when team members encounter unexpected challenges or results, they can do immediate problem solving and proactively identify when a result may be off-track.

***Example:*** *This email is important to the participants because many of them registered for this event to see specific speakers. Now that the schedules have changed, they are in danger of missing the sessions they most want to attend! This could upset participants; so much so that they might request refunds and complain to others in the facebook group—which could then become an event crisis. We want all the participants to easily attend the sessions they desire.*

3. **How will you (the recipient performing work) approach this and what do you need to be successful?**

   - **The "HOW"**
   - Agree on an approach, making sure that there is broad alignment.
   - Types of resources that will be needed—people, time, money, equipment, materials, etc.
   - Types of competencies or expertise that will be needed—specific skills, ability to focus for long periods of time, any analytical strengths, etc.
   - Types of support that may be needed—direct training, special access, involvement of experts, mentoring, new process or system, etc.
   - Considerations that may need addressing—prior commitments, workload issues, time constraints, special conditions, changing circumstances, etc.

When you are the delegator, you want the person taking on the responsibility (the recipient) to imagine themselves already doing the work you are assigning, and thinking through, "How am I going to approach this? And what do I really need to get this done successfully?"

***Example:*** *With all that I've shared about the email and why it's important, what might you need to get this email done successfully? Do you have the time, resources, and support to do this? Is there anyone else or other departments you need to involve? Any other support you might need?*

4. **What challenges might you encounter? How will you (we) respond to those?**

   - **The "WHAT IF'S"**
   - Unexpected or significant issues that could arise and harm our ability to achieve the result—obstacles, conflicting priorities, resource changes, etc.
   - Cooperation or coordination issues with other people or departments.
   - Critical timelines in danger of being broken.

We consider this the "engagement step" because the recipient has to proactively think about not only doing the tasks, but also anticipate what might get in the way of having success with this new responsibility. This requires thinking critically about the whole business picture and their broader role, along with the new responsibility, which then allows them to identify and discuss possible challenges up front, thus increasing the likelihood of success!

***Example:*** *Any other challenges or major issues you anticipate that may affect you completing this email? How will you let me know about those and are there any that we might want to form a "Plan B" for ahead of time? What about significant unexpected changes—how should we connect if those come up?*

5. **How will we monitor and/or follow up on progress? How will you (we) respond to unexpected challenges and urgent issues?**
    - **"The Recovery"**
    - Agree on times to connect for monitoring progress.
    - Plan for the unexpected—what you will do if serious issues erupt between agreed meetings.
        - Have designated "go to" people when a problem or challenge occurs.
        - Prepare contingency plans for high stakes goals.
    - Model Self-Leadership. (Avoid self-protective behaviors and emotionally reacting to situations and people.)

As the delegator, make sure to pre-schedule follow ups and check-ins for progress, along with a clear method to connect for urgent issues. Your stress level will decrease when you can trust how/when they will let you know if things don't go according to plan. This frees you up to focus on your other work instead of constantly wondering if you need to check on the person performing the task.

***Example:*** *When can we follow up on how the email is going? Since it's critical to get done in the next 24 hours, how about if we briefly connect* *three hours from now? And please text me if you get stuck or can't continue for any reason.*

6. **How will you know when the work is complete and the result has been achieved?**
   - **"The Finish"**
   - Confirm that the recipient will inform you when the work is complete and that it achieved the intended result(s).
   - It is important that the person doing the work takes responsibility for letting you know when it is complete, so that you don't have to ask!
   - When complete, the delegator can then acknowledge and appreciate the recipient who executed the work.
   - Fostering a culture of appreciation is one of the most effective and least costly things you can do to increase the productivity and performance of your team.

This step closes the loop so the delegator can stop tracking and thinking about the result.

Using the delegation formula allows leaders to "let go" of their worry and trust that the person doing the work has what they need, and if anything doesn't go as planned, that the delegator will be informed in time to resolve issues and still achieve the result.

***Example:*** *After we meet and review the email, you don't need to show it to me again when the graphics department adds their part. You can then have it sent out by the email team. Please let me know when it goes out and send me a copy of the final email.*

After it sends, remember that a little appreciation goes a long way!

***Example:*** *Thank you so much for your efforts, it turned out great! I'm now confident that everyone will get to see their favorite speakers, all thanks to you. I appreciate your attention to all the details and how you coordinated everything to make it happen.*

To make an effective agreement, these six steps must be clear to all involved. We encourage you to walk through each step, actually use the script (until it's habitual), especially when delegating significant responsibilities.

When people focus on the steps of the delegation process, their "thinking brain" is highly engaged and it becomes less likely that emotions drive the conversation. Share the script steps with your team members so they understand that this is a teamwork norm.

**Delegation is Active—Not Passive!**

When the person who will perform the tasks is engaged in making the commitment/agreement, it takes the pressure off the delegator to do the agreement process perfectly. This also allows the recipient to take more ownership in making the agreement since they will be a major player in getting it done.

It follows then, that the recipient should be fully empowered to "back-lead" the delegation process. When the recipient drives the agreement-making process and discussion; they don't need to worry if their supervisor forgets to share important context, or fails to establish a deadline. The recipient is empowered and expected to ask. This is a game-changer for delegation, as it places the main responsibility with the person who is producing the result—naturally creating more effective and reliable agreements. This alleviates the delegator from the burden of getting things exactly right. Ultimately, this engages everyone's critical thinking.

**Recipient-led Delegation in 6 Steps**

1. My understanding of the intended outcome is ______________.
2. The purpose and benefits are ______________________.
3. I intend to approach it this way: ______________________ and I need the following resources/ people/ support to be successful ______________________.

4. I anticipate the following challenges: ________________. I intend to respond to these challenges in this way: ____________.
5. I will follow up with you (when/how) ____________. I will surface significant and urgent issues (when/how). ____________.
6. I will let you know when it's complete and how it turned out (when/how). ____________.

The most effective teams are super proactive about teaching all their team members recipient-led delegation. They usually begin by utilizing these actual scripts as a guide when teaching/learning until everyone is able to habitually follow the process without needing the written guide. Because this is so important to team productivity, it's something that we recommend including in your on-boarding and training process.

We encourage you to begin implementing this new approach to delegation right away. Effective delegation leads to more trust and higher performance as more and more things get done "right" the first time. This means that you, the entrepreneur, will no longer have to "do everything important yourself." With protocols to delegate responsibility, you are free to do the higher-level strategic duties that only you can do.

There's no better time than the present to build a new, game-changing leadership habit. Use the structure of our scripts and the Conscious Agreement-making process to keep your teamwork focused on the Business Part—achieving the outcomes that matter.

Download printable copies of the delegation scripts:

**https://leadingedgeteams.com/delegation-download/**

"Clarity is critical."

—*ANNIE HYMAN PRATT*

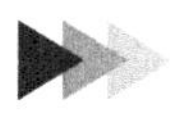

# Day 11

- Think of one new item/task/project you need to delegate. Who do you need to delegate it to? What is the successful outcome at completion? Make sure you fully understand this for yourself.

- Refer to Lesson #2 for details—prep for your delegation conversation by using the script below:

**Delegation Script—6 Steps**

1. The "What"
   The successful outcome looks like:
2. The "Why"
   The purpose and benefits are:
3. The "How"

How will you approach this and what do you need to be successful?

4. The "What if's"
   What challenges might you encounter? How will you (we) respond to those?
5. The "Recovery"
   How will you (we) follow up and respond to significant challenges and big breakdowns?
6. The "Finish"
   How will I know when the project or work is complete? Includes acknowledgement and appreciation from the delegator to the delegation recipient.

- Reach out and schedule your delegation conversation. Afterwards, take notes here about how it went, including anything you'd want to do differently in a future delegation.

- In the first 10 days of this journal process, we hope you noticed and acknowledged all the agreements around you, and got a sense of which agreements were working and which weren't. Have you identified any specific agreements you need to change or do differently in the future? If so, what were they?

- Did you gain any other insights into agreement-making that are altering your approach? What are those insights?

- Using the simple agreement formula, outline an agreement or request you've been thinking about raising with another team member. Now that you have the basic parts articulated, would you like to make the request? (say honestly yes or no—you're the only one who sees this workbook)

**Basic Agreement-Making Formula**

- What are you going for? (outcome)
- Why? (context/purpose it serves for the company)
- How? (my part, your part)
- What if? (if things go off track, how will we recover agreement?)

**Reminders:**

- Prepare a script for your delegations until it becomes a habit. Once you have the habit down you can reference it more as a quick checklist.
- Share the Delegation and Recipient-led Delegation scripts with your team. Having a clear process and building good delegation habits together will get the best results!
- Remember, delegation is a dual responsibility.

"Get neutral and intentional. You don't have a chance at making good choices if you don't anchor yourself in neutrality."

*—ANNIE HYMAN PRATT*

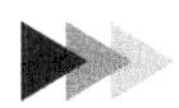

# Day 12

▶ Think of one new item/task/project you need to delegate. Who do you need to delegate it to? What is the successful outcome at completion? Make sure you fully understand this for yourself.

▶ Refer to Lesson #2 for details—prep for your delegation conversation by using the script below:

**Delegation Script—6 Steps**

1. The "What"
   The successful outcome looks like:
2. The "Why"
   The purpose and benefits are:
3. The "How"

How will you approach this and what do you need to be successful?

4. The "What if's"
   What challenges might you encounter? How will you (we) respond to those?
5. The "Recovery"
   How will you (we) follow up and respond to significant challenges and big breakdowns?
6. The "Finish"
   How will I know when the project or work is complete? Includes acknowledgement and appreciation from the delegator to the delegation recipient.

▶ Reach out and schedule your delegation conversation. Afterwards, take notes here about how it went, including anything you'd want to do differently in a future delegation.

▶ In the first 10 days of this journal process, we hope you noticed and acknowledged all the agreements around you, and got a sense of which agreements were working and which weren't. Have you identified any specific agreements you need to change or do differently in the future? If so, what were they?

▶ Did you gain any other insights into agreement-making that are altering your approach? What are those insights?

▶ Using the simple agreement formula, outline an agreement or request you've been thinking about raising with another team member. Now that you have the basic parts articulated, would you like to make the request? (say honestly yes or no—you're the only one who sees this workbook)

**Basic Agreement-Making Formula**

- What are you going for? (outcome)
- Why? (context/purpose it serves for the company)
- How? (my part, your part)
- What if? (if things go off track, how will we recover agreement?)

**Reminders:**

- Prepare a script for your delegations until it becomes a habit. Once you have the habit down you can reference it more as a quick checklist.
- Share the Delegation and Recipient-led Delegation scripts with your team. Having a clear process and building good delegation habits together will get the best results!
- Remember, delegation is a dual responsibility.

"An expectation is an implied agreement. Even a job description is an implied agreement."

*—ANNIE HYMAN PRATT*

# Day 13

- Think of one new item/task/project you need to delegate. Who do you need to delegate it to? What is the successful outcome at completion? Make sure you fully understand this for yourself.

- Refer to Lesson #2 for details—prep for your delegation conversation by using the script below:

**Delegation Script—6 Steps**

1. The "What"
   The successful outcome looks like:
2. The "Why"
   The purpose and benefits are:
3. The "How"

How will you approach this and what do you need to be successful?

4. The "What if's"
   What challenges might you encounter? How will you (we) respond to those?
5. The "Recovery"
   How will you (we) follow up and respond to significant challenges and big breakdowns?
6. The "Finish"
   How will I know when the project or work is complete? Includes acknowledgement and appreciation from the delegator to the delegation recipient.

▶ Reach out and schedule your delegation conversation. Afterwards, take notes here about how it went, including anything you'd want to do differently in a future delegation.

▶ In the first 10 days of this journal process, we hope you noticed and acknowledged all the agreements around you, and got a sense of which agreements were working and which weren't. Have you identified any specific agreements you need to change or do differently in the future? If so, what were they?

▶ Did you gain any other insights into agreement-making that are altering your approach? What are those insights?

- Using the simple agreement formula, outline an agreement or request you've been thinking about raising with another team member. Now that you have the basic parts articulated, would you like to make the request? (say honestly yes or no—you're the only one who sees this workbook)

### Basic Agreement-Making Formula

- What are you going for? (outcome)
- Why? (context/purpose it serves for the company)
- How? (my part, your part)
- What if? (if things go off track, how will we recover agreement?)

**Reminders:**

- Prepare a script for your delegations until it becomes a habit. Once you have the habit down you can reference it more as a quick checklist.
- Share the Delegation and Recipient-led Delegation scripts with your team. Having a clear process and building good delegation habits together will get the best results!
- Remember, delegation is a dual responsibility.

"Effective renegotiation is a leadership skill to master. In business things change and circumstances shift, which is why agreements are more complex than just keeping your word."

—*ANNIE HYMAN PRATT*

# Day 14

▶ Think of one new item/task/project you need to delegate. Who do you need to delegate it to? What is the successful outcome at completion? Make sure you fully understand this for yourself.

▶ Refer to Lesson #2 for details—prep for your delegation conversation by using the script below:

**Delegation Script—6 Steps**

1. The "What"
   The successful outcome looks like:
2. The "Why"
   The purpose and benefits are:
3. The "How"

How will you approach this and what do you need to be successful?

4. The "What if's"
   What challenges might you encounter? How will you (we) respond to those?
5. The "Recovery"
   How will you (we) follow up and respond to significant challenges and big breakdowns?
6. The "Finish"
   How will I know when the project or work is complete? Includes acknowledgement and appreciation from the delegator to the delegation recipient.

- ▶ Reach out and schedule your delegation conversation. Afterwards, take notes here about how it went, including anything you'd want to do differently in a future delegation.

- ▶ In the first 10 days of this journal process, we hope you noticed and acknowledged all the agreements around you, and got a sense of which agreements were working and which weren't. Have you identified any specific agreements you need to change or do differently in the future? If so, what were they?

- ▶ Did you gain any other insights into agreement-making that are altering your approach? What are those insights?

▶ Using the simple agreement formula, outline an agreement or request you've been thinking about raising with another team member. Now that you have the basic parts articulated, would you like to make the request? (say honestly yes or no—you're the only one who sees this workbook)

**Basic Agreement-Making Formula**

- What are you going for? (outcome)
- Why? (context/purpose it serves for the company)
- How? (my part, your part)
- What if? (if things go off track, how will we recover agreement?)

**Reminders:**

- Prepare a script for your delegations until it becomes a habit. Once you have the habit down you can reference it more as a quick checklist.
- Share the Delegation and Recipient-led Delegation scripts with your team. Having a clear process and building good delegation habits together will get the best results!
- Remember, delegation is a dual responsibility.

"Business is like a basketball pass—to play basketball together, you have to move the ball around. You can't play the game without passing—it's the same doing business and working as a team. You can't do business without making agreements."

—*ANNIE HYMAN PRATT*

# Day 15

- Think of one new item/task/project you need to delegate. Who do you need to delegate it to? What is the successful outcome at completion? Make sure you fully understand this for yourself.

- Refer to Lesson #2 for details—prep for your delegation conversation by using the script below:

**Delegation Script—6 Steps**

1. The "What"
   The successful outcome looks like:
2. The "Why"
   The purpose and benefits are:
3. The "How"

How will you approach this and what do you need to be successful?

4. The "What if's"
   What challenges might you encounter? How will you (we) respond to those?
5. The "Recovery"
   How will you (we) follow up and respond to significant challenges and big breakdowns?
6. The "Finish"
   How will I know when the project or work is complete? Includes acknowledgement and appreciation from the delegator to the delegation recipient.

- Reach out and schedule your delegation conversation. Afterwards, take notes here about how it went, including anything you'd want to do differently in a future delegation.

- In the first 10 days of this journal process, we hope you noticed and acknowledged all the agreements around you, and got a sense of which agreements were working and which weren't. Have you identified any specific agreements you need to change or do differently in the future? If so, what were they?

- Did you gain any other insights into agreement-making that are altering your approach? What are those insights?

▶ Using the simple agreement formula, outline an agreement or request you've been thinking about raising with another team member. Now that you have the basic parts articulated, would you like to make the request? (say honestly yes or no—you're the only one who sees this workbook)

**Basic Agreement-Making Formula**

- What are you going for? (outcome)
- Why? (context/purpose it serves for the company)
- How? (my part, your part)
- What if? (if things go off track, how will we recover agreement?)

**Reminders:**

- Prepare a script for your delegations until it becomes a habit. Once you have the habit down you can reference it more as a quick checklist.
- Share the Delegation and Recipient-led Delegation scripts with your team. Having a clear process and building good delegation habits together will get the best results!
- Remember, delegation is a dual responsibility.

"You, as a leader, need to create the conditions for people to do their most courageous thinking and acting."

—*ANNIE HYMAN PRATT*

# Day 16

- Think of one new item/task/project you need to delegate. Who do you need to delegate it to? What is the successful outcome at completion? Make sure you fully understand this for yourself.

- Refer to Lesson #2 for details—prep for your delegation conversation by using the script below:

**Delegation Script—6 Steps**

1. The "What"
   The successful outcome looks like:
2. The "Why"
   The purpose and benefits are:
3. The "How"

How will you approach this and what do you need to be successful?

4. The "What if's"
   What challenges might you encounter? How will you (we) respond to those?
5. The "Recovery"
   How will you (we) follow up and respond to significant challenges and big breakdowns?
6. The "Finish"
   How will I know when the project or work is complete? Includes acknowledgement and appreciation from the delegator to the delegation recipient.

- ▶ Reach out and schedule your delegation conversation. Afterwards, take notes here about how it went, including anything you'd want to do differently in a future delegation.

- ▶ In the first 10 days of this journal process, we hope you noticed and acknowledged all the agreements around you, and got a sense of which agreements were working and which weren't. Have you identified any specific agreements you need to change or do differently in the future? If so, what were they?

- ▶ Did you gain any other insights into agreement-making that are altering your approach? What are those insights?

▶ Using the simple agreement formula, outline an agreement or request you've been thinking about raising with another team member. Now that you have the basic parts articulated, would you like to make the request? (say honestly yes or no—you're the only one who sees this workbook)

**Basic Agreement-Making Formula**

- What are you going for? (outcome)
- Why? (context/purpose it serves for the company)
- How? (my part, your part)
- What if? (if things go off track, how will we recover agreement?)

**Reminders:**

- Prepare a script for your delegations until it becomes a habit. Once you have the habit down you can reference it more as a quick checklist.
- Share the Delegation and Recipient-led Delegation scripts with your team. Having a clear process and building good delegation habits together will get the best results!
- Remember, delegation is a dual responsibility.

"If we think of agreement-making as an issue of integrity, it is too easy to beat ourselves up—which is a habit that damages our confidence and brings us no closer to achieving results!"

*—ANNIE HYMAN PRATT*

# Day 17

- Think of one new item/task/project you need to delegate. Who do you need to delegate it to? What is the successful outcome at completion? Make sure you fully understand this for yourself.

- Refer to Lesson #2 for details—prep for your delegation conversation by using the script below:

**Delegation Script—6 Steps**

1. The "What"
   The successful outcome looks like:
2. The "Why"
   The purpose and benefits are:
3. The "How"

How will you approach this and what do you need to be successful?

4. The "What if's"
   What challenges might you encounter? How will you (we) respond to those?
5. The "Recovery"
   How will you (we) follow up and respond to significant challenges and big breakdowns?
6. The "Finish"
   How will I know when the project or work is complete? Includes acknowledgement and appreciation from the delegator to the delegation recipient.

- Reach out and schedule your delegation conversation. Afterwards, take notes here about how it went, including anything you'd want to do differently in a future delegation.

- In the first 10 days of this journal process, we hope you noticed and acknowledged all the agreements around you, and got a sense of which agreements were working and which weren't. Have you identified any specific agreements you need to change or do differently in the future? If so, what were they?

- Did you gain any other insights into agreement-making that are altering your approach? What are those insights?

▶ Using the simple agreement formula, outline an agreement or request you've been thinking about raising with another team member. Now that you have the basic parts articulated, would you like to make the request? (say honestly yes or no—you're the only one who sees this workbook)

**Basic Agreement-Making Formula**

- What are you going for? (outcome)
- Why? (context/purpose it serves for the company)
- How? (my part, your part)
- What if? (if things go off track, how will we recover agreement?)

**Reminders:**

- Prepare a script for your delegations until it becomes a habit. Once you have the habit down you can reference it more as a quick checklist.
- Share the Delegation and Recipient-led Delegation scripts with your team. Having a clear process and building good delegation habits together will get the best results!
- Remember, delegation is a dual responsibility.

"There's a difference between rescue and support. Rescue robs the other person of the opportunity to grow."

—*ANNIE HYMAN PRATT*

# Day 18

▶ Think of one new item/task/project you need to delegate. Who do you need to delegate it to? What is the successful outcome at completion? Make sure you fully understand this for yourself.

▶ Refer to Lesson #2 for details—prep for your delegation conversation by using the script below:

**Delegation Script—6 Steps**

1. The "What"
   The successful outcome looks like:
2. The "Why"
   The purpose and benefits are:
3. The "How"

How will you approach this and what do you need to be successful?

4. The "What if's"
   What challenges might you encounter? How will you (we) respond to those?
5. The "Recovery"
   How will you (we) follow up and respond to significant challenges and big breakdowns?
6. The "Finish"
   How will I know when the project or work is complete? Includes acknowledgement and appreciation from the delegator to the delegation recipient.

- Reach out and schedule your delegation conversation. Afterwards, take notes here about how it went, including anything you'd want to do differently in a future delegation.

- In the first 10 days of this journal process, we hope you noticed and acknowledged all the agreements around you, and got a sense of which agreements were working and which weren't. Have you identified any specific agreements you need to change or do differently in the future? If so, what were they?

- Did you gain any other insights into agreement-making that are altering your approach? What are those insights?

▶ Using the simple agreement formula, outline an agreement or request you've been thinking about raising with another team member. Now that you have the basic parts articulated, would you like to make the request? (say honestly yes or no—you're the only one who sees this workbook)

**Basic Agreement-Making Formula**

- What are you going for? (outcome)
- Why? (context/purpose it serves for the company)
- How? (my part, your part)
- What if? (if things go off track, how will we recover agreement?)

**Reminders:**

- Prepare a script for your delegations until it becomes a habit. Once you have the habit down you can reference it more as a quick checklist.
- Share the Delegation and Recipient-led Delegation scripts with your team. Having a clear process and building good delegation habits together will get the best results!
- Remember, delegation is a dual responsibility.

"When you show up as an 'A+' Leader, you take leadership dialogue to heart!"

*—ANNIE HYMAN PRATT*

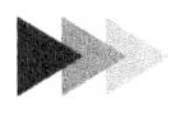

# Day 19

▶ Think of one new item/task/project you need to delegate. Who do you need to delegate it to? What is the successful outcome at completion? Make sure you fully understand this for yourself.

▶ Refer to Lesson #2 for details—prep for your delegation conversation by using the script below:

**Delegation Script—6 Steps**

1. The "What"
   The successful outcome looks like:
2. The "Why"
   The purpose and benefits are:
3. The "How"

How will you approach this and what do you need to be successful?

4. The "What if's"
   What challenges might you encounter? How will you (we) respond to those?
5. The "Recovery"
   How will you (we) follow up and respond to significant challenges and big breakdowns?
6. The "Finish"
   How will I know when the project or work is complete? Includes acknowledgement and appreciation from the delegator to the delegation recipient.

- Reach out and schedule your delegation conversation. Afterwards, take notes here about how it went, including anything you'd want to do differently in a future delegation.

- In the first 10 days of this journal process, we hope you noticed and acknowledged all the agreements around you, and got a sense of which agreements were working and which weren't. Have you identified any specific agreements you need to change or do differently in the future? If so, what were they?

- Did you gain any other insights into agreement-making that are altering your approach? What are those insights?

- Using the simple agreement formula, outline an agreement or request you've been thinking about raising with another team member. Now that you have the basic parts articulated, would you like to make the request? (say honestly yes or no—you're the only one who sees this workbook)

**Basic Agreement-Making Formula**

- What are you going for? (outcome)
- Why? (context/purpose it serves for the company)
- How? (my part, your part)
- What if? (if things go off track, how will we recover agreement?)

**Reminders:**

- Prepare a script for your delegations until it becomes a habit. Once you have the habit down you can reference it more as a quick checklist.
- Share the Delegation and Recipient-led Delegation scripts with your team. Having a clear process and building good delegation habits together will get the best results!
- Remember, delegation is a dual responsibility.

"In giving direction, context is King. People need to know why they're doing what they're doing so they can be their own problem solvers. The whole point is to empower others to take great action toward a result."

—ANNIE HYMAN PRATT

# Day 20

▶ Think of one new item/task/project you need to delegate. Who do you need to delegate it to? What is the successful outcome at completion? Make sure you fully understand this for yourself.

▶ Refer to Lesson #2 for details—prep for your delegation conversation by using the script below:

**Delegation Script—6 Steps**

1. The "What"
   The successful outcome looks like:
2. The "Why"
   The purpose and benefits are:
3. The "How"

How will you approach this and what do you need to be successful?

4. The "What if's"
   What challenges might you encounter? How will you (we) respond to those?
5. The "Recovery"
   How will you (we) follow up and respond to significant challenges and big breakdowns?
6. The "Finish"
   How will I know when the project or work is complete? Includes acknowledgement and appreciation from the delegator to the delegation recipient.

- Reach out and schedule your delegation conversation. Afterwards, take notes here about how it went, including anything you'd want to do differently in a future delegation.

- In the first 10 days of this journal process, we hope you noticed and acknowledged all the agreements around you, and got a sense of which agreements were working and which weren't. Have you identified any specific agreements you need to change or do differently in the future? If so, what were they?

- Did you gain any other insights into agreement-making that are altering your approach? What are those insights?

- Using the simple agreement formula, outline an agreement or request you've been thinking about raising with another team member. Now that you have the basic parts articulated, would you like to make the request? (say honestly yes or no—you're the only one who sees this workbook)

### Basic Agreement-Making Formula

- What are you going for? (outcome)
- Why? (context/purpose it serves for the company)
- How? (my part, your part)
- What if? (if things go off track, how will we recover agreement?)

**Reminders:**

- Prepare a script for your delegations until it becomes a habit. Once you have the habit down you can reference it more as a quick checklist.
- Share the Delegation and Recipient-led Delegation scripts with your team. Having a clear process and building good delegation habits together will get the best results!
- Remember, delegation is a dual responsibility.

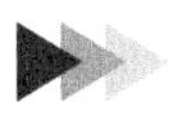

# 20-Day Check-in

*Making Agreements—Conscious Agreements—Delegation*

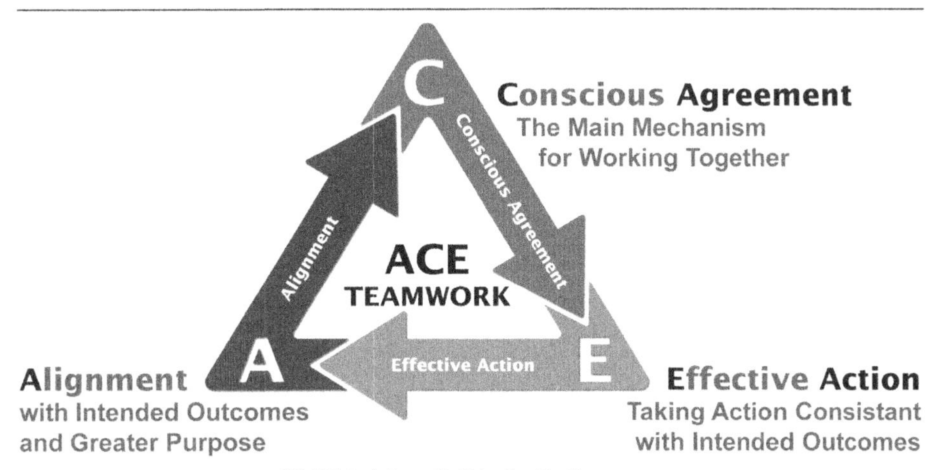

- Are you making agreements differently than how you made them before? What benefits do you see from your new approach?

- What wins did you experience when practicing your conscious agreement-making skills these past 10 days?

- What are you noticing about yourself and your leadership? Where do you most see agreements serving to strengthen your individual performance and the team's performance?

- To what degree do you feel you have now mastered using the delegation and recipient-led delegation scripts? What will you do to continue improving?

- Have you identified any higher level agreements that need to be implemented or renegotiated to support the whole team and the company? If so, what do they involve?

Download a printable copy of The Basics of Agreements

**https://leadingedgeteams.com/agreements-download/**

SECTION 3

# Things Change: Agreements In The Real World

WHEN YOU CAN'T FIGURE OUT HOW TO SAY ANYTHING OTHER THAN YES

"People are very open-minded about new things, as long as they're exactly like the old ones."

*–CHARLES F. KETTERING*

# Lesson 3

You've now practiced making agreements for twenty days. Congratulations! We have ten more to go in this journal... and after 20 days of practice, we're confident that you will already be noticing major improvements and wins when making agreements with your team. However, Lesson 3 is essential to complete, because agreements are rarely "made once and done"—there are too many things in business that continually change and you are unable to anticipate them—so the likelihood of needing to re-examine and adjust agreements is large. This section is all about *renegotiating* agreements and working with change.

**Constant Change And Ongoing Renegotiation**

Sustainable success in business requires skill to perform in uncertainty and never ending change. This is "the game of business," and victory doesn't come easy! As a business owner or leader, each day you're confronted with new challenges. Not only do you need to respond to changes outside your business, but you'll take on new endeavors (which never go perfectly according to plan), work with humans (who have needs and constraints), and deal with a myriad of problems and mistakes. Sometimes I reflect on this and think it's a miracle that any business survives at all!

Keep in mind that as you build secure relationships and a psychologically safe environment in your ACE Team, you are also maneuvering through each day's unexpected twists and turns. You may encounter a sudden change (internally or externally); customer demands might require you to revamp your service or product; a valued team member might quit and now you need a replacement; or you might get hit with a pandemic where everything gets upended.

As an entrepreneurial business, you live and breathe change and are subject to the emotional rollercoaster that leaders must endure. Fortunately, utilizing the CcORE Process will provide clarity and smooth out the ride to help you stay centered and effective.

**The Myth of the Business "Hole In One"**

So, here's the deal. It is a myth that a business owner can plan something really, really well, tell people exactly what to do at the outset of a new project, and have perfect success by following the exact original plan. I believe this occurs about as often as golfers make a hole in one.

The reality is more like everyday amateur golf—you plan your shot, intending to get as close as possible to the pin—you hit the ball, see it land not exactly where you had hoped, and then plan your next shot. Developing people that are able to adjust their "shots" as progress and circumstances unfold is one of the most important—and hardest—parts of business leadership.

Seriously—do you remember ever coordinating a hugely important project where everything went perfectly? Even after breaking the task down into its component parts and delegating to team members, did everyone get their work in before the deadline without working overtime and without having to raise any issues or propose changes (big or small)?

With ongoing change being the "rule" (not the exception), renegotiating then becomes your primary means of "changing course." And hey, sometimes you are right on; you might one day get a hole in one! But the bigger likelihood is that you learn how to systematically make and renegotiate agreements so that you consistently achieve PAR and hopefully a lot of birdies :)

Because agreement-making is so much more complex than people realize, mastering it requires some unique skills that we don't usually associate with making agreements. We touched on many of these earlier, but we're going to explore them deeper in this section because they're so fundamental to not only making original agreements but also to renegotiating.

However, we do recognize that not keeping original agreements, no matter the reason, feels terrible; it's because humans often perceive keeping agreements and commitments as a matter of integrity. But I need you to hear this: to get results in business, you cannot relate to agreements in this way!

It's helpful to go back to a sports analogy—you may have heard this quote from Michael Jordan:

> I've missed more than 9000 shots in my career. I've lost almost 300 games. 26 times, I've been trusted to take the game winning shot and missed. I've failed over and over and over again in my life. And that is why I succeed.

The world is changing faster and faster in ways that impact our businesses, which means we have to respond with equal speed. Individuals must be nimble and make smart judgements about company decisions, and this requires an ever higher level of coordination and cooperation excellence carried out through agreements. Just waiting for the higher ups to relay solutions won't cut it: team members need the collaboration and critical thinking to find these solutions themselves!

### Secure Relationships—the Bedrock of Renegotiation

Fortunately, when people experience a secure working relationship, they are able to drop their guard and avoid the self-protective thoughts and behaviors that sabotage making agreements, changing agreements and carrying them out.

So, your goal as a CEO/entrepreneur/leader is to create a safe environment by fostering relationships and modeling interactions where you consistently demonstrate care, respect, and take into account other team member's interests. You will know that you've achieved a safe environment when: team members speak honestly in tense situations, share differing opinions respectfully, disclose fears and feelings, offer novel ideas, and are able to change their position when new information arises.

**Here's how you can promote psychological safety and secure relationships:**

- Set clear (and reasonable!) expectations
- Check that each member has the necessary resources
- Make mutual agreements, including making requests without pressuring
- Talk tentatively—ask open-ended questions
- Listen actively—respect their point-of-view
- Acknowledge facts, challenges and uncertainties
- Meet feelings with empathy and compassion
- Walk in their shoes for awhile
- Express confidence in them
- Show interest in their well-being
- Repair tense situations ASAP
- Take responsibility for you and your part in any issue

However, as you implement the above list, keep in mind that providing psychological safety does NOT mean providing comfort and eliminating challenges. The whole point of psychological safety is to enable people to handle more risk, stress and responsibility as they are able to trust that their teammates "have their back" and will look out for their interests. This allows team members to take the focus and energy they would have put into "watching their backs" (self-protecting), and together put energy into achieving business results.

**Renegotiating is Easier than You Think!**

There are two main elements to keep in mind when you renegotiate an agreement, change expectations, or change any plans that people have already agreed to.

First, people are naturally invested in agreements they've already made, because they take considerable time, focus, mental and emotional energy to create. No one wants to have all that work upended just to re-invest in coming up with another agreement that will hopefully work. It can feel like a waste of time and resources if the first agreement wasn't going to stick. But it's NOT a waste of time—which we'll talk about shortly.

So to renegotiate effectively, you've got to **demonstrate respect for your teammates' time and energy** and truly care about reaching a win-win agreement each time, no matter how many times you come back to the negotiating table.

The second thing to keep in mind is that people need **succinct context and the relevant, organized new information** so that adjusting an agreement is as easy as possible.

**The Key to Renegotiating (Almost) Anything in Business:**

***Start with "WHAT CHANGED" in the situation, including how it makes the current agreement no longer effective.***

- Here's what's changed; most important to state (circumstances, why it's not working as expected or planned)
- Here's what's changed on my side (your situation or new awareness)
- Now I'm thinking we do "y" instead of "x" (proactive problem-solving suggestions)

To answer these questions effectively, you need to be sure you fully understand the outcome you are going for. Renegotiations' purpose is to get us back on track so that we can successfully reach the outcome.

Sometimes the big picture outcome changes as a result of a shift we weren't expecting. That is exactly why good agreements are not rigid and have the expectation of change built into them.

Don't misunderstand, agreements are meant to be relied upon, but our agreements stand on the most solid ground when we know that if something big changes, we follow a protocol. Keeping communication open to surface challenges, new discoveries, and shifting landscapes is at the heart of ACE teamwork. To be effective, agreements must reflect the current situation so that we can have the best plan of action to reach the outcomes.

The important part of renegotiation, the step you cannot miss, is making sure that you leave the exchange with a clearly articulated NEW AGREEMENT.

That is why understanding how to make strong agreements is a fundamental leadership skill that you must strengthen. As you renegotiate, you need to address all the elements of the agreement formula so that you and the team create new clarity and alignment on how to best reach the intended outcome.

Remember, change happens, don't be afraid to renegotiate! It is a fundamental part of using the tool of agreements effectively. When you embrace challenge and change, your entire experience of business and teamwork will change for the better, and both the Business Part and the People Part of your organization will thrive!

"Agreements are a process, not a promise."

*—ANNIE HYMAN PRATT*

# Day 21

- Remember, agreements are a process and not a promise. Is there anything on your plate you are thinking you may need to renegotiate? Given the current facts of the situation, what may be the shift that is needed to expectations, timelines, etc.?

- What new adjusted agreement do you think would help you better deliver the results? Where will you need to raise the gap you are seeing and renegotiate?

▶ Psychological Safety is a key to high performance. How can you make it safe for yourself and others as you move through this renegotiation? Remember to put yourself in the other person's shoes, what might they most be concerned about? What context would be helpful to share in order to mitigate those concerns?

▶ What other agreements might your new agreement impact?

- In the process of strengthening your use of agreements (your main mechanism for working with your team)—what is your biggest learning today?

"Accept that tomorrow may force you to pivot."

*—ANNIE HYMAN PRATT*

# Day 22

- Remember, agreements are a process and not a promise. Is there anything on your plate you are thinking you may need to renegotiate? Given the current facts of the situation, what may be the shift that is needed to expectations, timelines, etc.?

- What new adjusted agreement do you think would help you better deliver the results? Where will you need to raise the gap you are seeing and renegotiate?

- Psychological Safety is a key to high performance. How can you make it safe for yourself and others as you move through this renegotiation? Remember to put yourself in the other person's shoes, what might they most be concerned about? What context would be helpful to share in order to mitigate those concerns?

- What other agreements might your new agreement impact?

- In the process of strengthening your use of agreements (your main mechanism for working with your team)—what is your biggest learning today?

"Recovery plans are an essential part of good agreements, because in the heat of the moment, the team already knows how to pivot."

*—ANNIE HYMAN PRATT*

# Day 23

- Remember, agreements are a process and not a promise. Is there anything on your plate you are thinking you may need to renegotiate? Given the current facts of the situation, what may be the shift that is needed to expectations, timelines, etc.?

- What new adjusted agreement do you think would help you better deliver the results? Where will you need to raise the gap you are seeing and renegotiate?

- Psychological Safety is a key to high performance. How can you make it safe for yourself and others as you move through this renegotiation? Remember to put yourself in the other person's shoes, what might they most be concerned about? What context would be helpful to share in order to mitigate those concerns?

- What other agreements might your new agreement impact?

- In the process of strengthening your use of agreements (your main mechanism for working with your team)—what is your biggest learning today?

"Control is the master addiction."

*—ANNIE HYMAN PRATT*

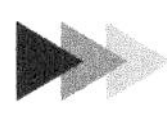

# Day 24

- Remember, agreements are a process and not a promise. Is there anything on your plate you are thinking you may need to renegotiate? Given the current facts of the situation, what may be the shift that is needed to expectations, timelines, etc.?

- What new adjusted agreement do you think would help you better deliver the results? Where will you need to raise the gap you are seeing and renegotiate?

- Psychological Safety is a key to high performance. How can you make it safe for yourself and others as you move through this renegotiation? Remember to put yourself in the other person's shoes, what might they most be concerned about? What context would be helpful to share in order to mitigate those concerns?

- What other agreements might your new agreement impact?

- In the process of strengthening your use of agreements (your main mechanism for working with your team)—what is your biggest learning today?

"Making change and actually not imploding—being able to move through the change without creating havoc—is an extraordinary win."

—*ANNIE HYMAN PRATT*

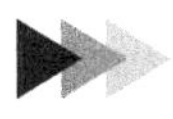

# Day 25

- Remember, agreements are a process and not a promise. Is there anything on your plate you are thinking you may need to renegotiate? Given the current facts of the situation, what may be the shift that is needed to expectations, timelines, etc.?

- What new adjusted agreement do you think would help you better deliver the results? Where will you need to raise the gap you are seeing and renegotiate?

- Psychological Safety is a key to high performance. How can you make it safe for yourself and others as you move through this renegotiation? Remember to put yourself in the other person's shoes, what might they most be concerned about? What context would be helpful to share in order to mitigate those concerns?

- What other agreements might your new agreement impact?

▶ In the process of strengthening your use of agreements (your main mechanism for working with your team)—what is your biggest learning today?

“'A+' Leaders prepare and pause before they enter into a conversation.”

*—ANNIE HYMAN PRATT*

# Day 26

- Remember, agreements are a process and not a promise. Is there anything on your plate you are thinking you may need to renegotiate? Given the current facts of the situation, what may be the shift that is needed to expectations, timelines, etc.?

- What new adjusted agreement do you think would help you better deliver the results? Where will you need to raise the gap you are seeing and renegotiate?

- Psychological Safety is a key to high performance. How can you make it safe for yourself and others as you move through this renegotiation? Remember to put yourself in the other person's shoes, what might they most be concerned about? What context would be helpful to share in order to mitigate those concerns?

- What other agreements might your new agreement impact?

- In the process of strengthening your use of agreements (your main mechanism for working with your team)—what is your biggest learning today?

"Another reason to resist judging others—it reminds you to resist judging yourself."

—*ANNIE HYMAN PRATT*

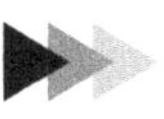

# Day 27

- Remember, agreements are a process and not a promise. Is there anything on your plate you are thinking you may need to renegotiate? Given the current facts of the situation, what may be the shift that is needed to expectations, timelines, etc.?

- What new adjusted agreement do you think would help you better deliver the results? Where will you need to raise the gap you are seeing and renegotiate?

- Psychological Safety is a key to high performance. How can you make it safe for yourself and others as you move through this renegotiation? Remember to put yourself in the other person's shoes, what might they most be concerned about? What context would be helpful to share in order to mitigate those concerns?

- What other agreements might your new agreement impact?

- In the process of strengthening your use of agreements (your main mechanism for working with your team)—what is your biggest learning today?

"Business as usual includes constant challenge and change, which requires ongoing growth and learning."

*—ANNIE HYMAN PRATT*

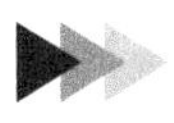

# Day 28

- Remember, agreements are a process and not a promise. Is there anything on your plate you are thinking you may need to renegotiate? Given the current facts of the situation, what may be the shift that is needed to expectations, timelines, etc.?

- What new adjusted agreement do you think would help you better deliver the results? Where will you need to raise the gap you are seeing and renegotiate?

- Psychological Safety is a key to high performance. How can you make it safe for yourself and others as you move through this renegotiation? Remember to put yourself in the other person's shoes, what might they most be concerned about? What context would be helpful to share in order to mitigate those concerns?

- What other agreements might your new agreement impact?

- In the process of strengthening your use of agreements (your main mechanism for working with your team)—what is your biggest learning today?

"When you have a strong recovery plan,
safety is a positive side effect."

—*ANNIE HYMAN PRATT*

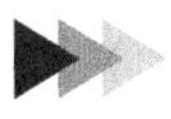

# Day 29

- Remember, agreements are a process and not a promise. Is there anything on your plate you are thinking you may need to renegotiate? Given the current facts of the situation, what may be the shift that is needed to expectations, timelines, etc.?

- What new adjusted agreement do you think would help you better deliver the results? Where will you need to raise the gap you are seeing and renegotiate?

- Psychological Safety is a key to high performance. How can you make it safe for yourself and others as you move through this renegotiation? Remember to put yourself in the other person's shoes, what might they most be concerned about? What context would be helpful to share in order to mitigate those concerns?

- What other agreements might your new agreement impact?

- In the process of strengthening your use of agreements (your main mechanism for working with your team)—what is your biggest learning today?

"Change is the *only* constant."

—*ANNIE HYMAN PRATT*

# Day 30

- Remember, agreements are a process and not a promise. Is there anything on your plate you are thinking you may need to renegotiate? Given the current facts of the situation, what may be the shift that is needed to expectations, timelines, etc.?

- What new adjusted agreement do you think would help you better deliver the results? Where will you need to raise the gap you are seeing and renegotiate?

- Psychological Safety is a key to high performance. How can you make it safe for yourself and others as you move through this renegotiation? Remember to put yourself in the other person's shoes, what might they most be concerned about? What context would be helpful to share in order to mitigate those concerns?

- What other agreements might your new agreement impact?

- In the process of strengthening your use of agreements (your main mechanism for working with your team)—what is your biggest learning today?

# 30-Day Check-in

## *When Agreements Cannot Be Met—Renegotiate!*

**Moving from Authority and Control to Unified Team Driven Results**

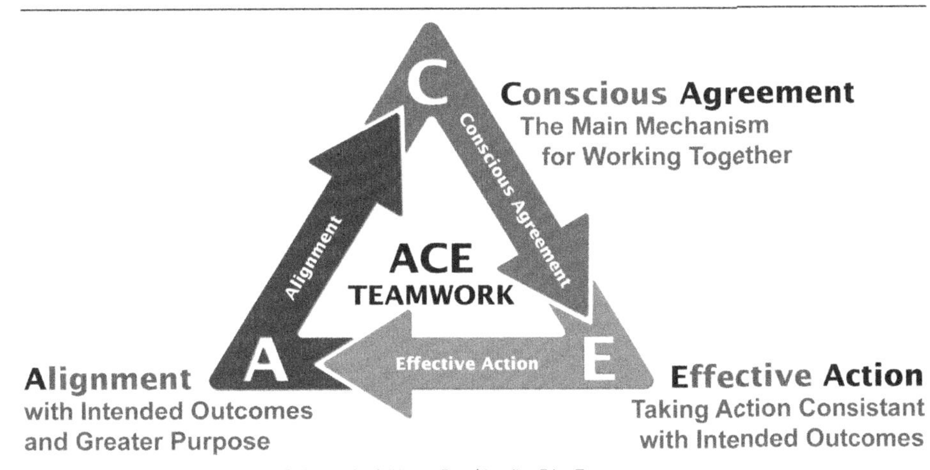

'A+' Leaders recognize that they use agreements everyday, and consciously use them as a tool to get the results they are after for the greater needs of the business.

- What has changed most in the last 30 days in how you utilize agreements?

- Where do you see further growth opportunities in your use of conscious agreement-making (with yourself, the team, and/or your CEO)?

- What agreements would you like to make with yourself today to support your leadership development?

Remember, agreements are like a basketball pass. They are how you move things down the court and ultimately win the game. And like a basketball pass they are easy when the situation is easy, but harder when playing the championship game. Leadership mastery requires ongoing strengthening of your skills. Meaning that your agreements must get stronger and stronger so that you can make a successful pass under heightened stress and pressure. No one player loses the game at the buzzer—help your team make the winning shot!

# Before you go, you must know how to Repair and Apologize

## Agreements Don't Always Work Out...

When teams take shortcuts in making agreements or a project gets committed to before everyone understands the impacts, big challenges ensue. This is where the team has to stop and go back to the drawing board, revisiting all the planning and decisions they already made. This is especially frustrating because shortcuts actually increase the time, focus and energy needed to achieve success.

Rushing a decision or project, not giving it the time it deserves, or flying solo without gathering team input is a crisis waiting to happen. These situations easily snowball into damaged relationships, trust being broken, and resources being strained as others' self-protective behaviors rise up and take over.

**The destructive cycle looks like this:**

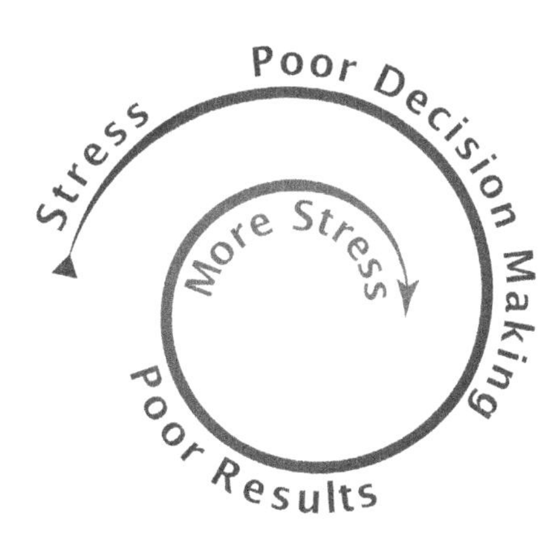


The only way to stop this cycle is to take ownership by getting yourself out of self-protection (by pausing and working the CcORE Empowerment Process). Then repair any relationships that lack trust or have been meaningfully damaged.

### There are Two Forms of Repair:

1. **When tensions rise but people are still cooperating**: Re-establish the psychological safety and affirm the commitment by showing that you care about how things turn out for them.
   - Use affirming words and actions to bring tension down.
   - Hold safe space for the other person, so they have the opportunity to self-regulate.
   - Listen. Allow the other person to share their feelings. (Even just naming a feeling de-escalates an emotional situation and engages the logical thinking brain.)
2. **When the relationship experiences a big drop in trust** and people are feeling hurt or disrespected, a sincere apology is the next step to repair it. Apology is not an admission of guilt; it is a well-intended form of repair. It is how you take responsibility for your actions and their impact on the other person.

## The Power Of Apology

Apology is your way to take responsibility for what you contributed to (or withheld from) a problem, disagreement or conflict. Think of it as how YOU can communicate what you wish YOU had done differently in the situation that could have made things better.

When communicated appropriately, apology is one of the most effective relationship tools. Every human being possesses it, and yet very, very few people utilize it effectively or often enough! People are usually worried that if they apologize, it'll be perceived as an admission of fault or guilt that will be used against them, or that the other person will use the admission to excuse their own underperformance and avoid accountability. Annie freely admits, "I myself had this mistaken understanding for years!"

The truth is that an apology is a generous way for you to "go first" in taking responsibility and resolving an issue, which relieves tension and lowers the risk of conflict. When tension eases and self-protection decreases, the situation can be seen more clearly. It then allows a situation to be discussed in a way that makes it easier for both parties to take ownership of their parts and move forward to agree on a solution.

Sometimes, offering an apology is the only way to calm a situation enough to move forward. In many instances, withholding an apology leaves both parties worse off!

**It is important to remember...**

*An Apology is NOT about you!*

It's about repairing and restoring the relationship, not about defending or establishing who is right or wrong. To be a bit more precise, for the person apologizing, it's about communicating that you genuinely care about the impact *your behavior and actions* had on the other person.

**Steps of Apology:**

1. When I did or said (or didn't do or say) ________________(my behavior), I know it impacted you ___________(acknowledge the impact).
2. I am sorry. I do care about how things turn out for you.
3. I'll do it differently in the future by _____________ (new behavior or response)

Download a printable copy of our Secret Recipe

**https://leadingedgeteams.com/secret-recipe/**

# Congratulations

### *Our Wish For You...*

Now that you've learned ACE Team Agreements and how to apply them in your company, we're confident you will make effective conscious agreements and achieve amazing results—as if you have an ever present "ace in the hole" to play whenever it's needed.

We hope that your dedication to improving your leadership skills not only increases your business results, but that you also experience the joy and fulfillment that comes only when working with a team of people that are successful together!

We also hope that any doubts or reservations you've had as a leader continuously fall away, and that you fall in love with your role of leading and developing others! By embracing your leadership, you are contributing so much more than just a job to peoples' lives—you're helping them become the best version of themselves.

# Next Steps

As in all things, there's always more to learn, further leadership and team development to anticipate, and methods to apply that solve a problem. Watch for the next journal in our "Self-Leadership Series", available 2021: *How to Get Performance Back On Track with The Gappa Formula*.

ACTIONS:

1. Download all suggested materials in this journal and keep handy for your reference.
2. At Leading Edge Teams we are committed to supporting your leadership growth. If you have questions about applying agreements to your business, or want to learn how you can work with us directly, visit our website to get an introductory coaching call as our gift to you.

**https://leadingedgeteams.com/schedule/**

# Annie Hyman Pratt

Annie Hyman Pratt is the master at developing leaders and teams that drive rapid and sustainable results—so entrepreneurs can work on the strategic and visionary aspects of their business—and have the time, freedom, and the impact they desire. Annie more than 10x'd her family business—The Coffee Bean and Tea Leaf—taking it from seven domestic "Mom and Pop Shops" to an International Brand of 70+ stores, all in seven years time. She then led the company through a highly successful sale.

Annie spent the next two decades as a top-tier business consultant specializing in "Rapid Growth and Change." She has since worked with 50+ companies—in diverse industries—guiding them through virtually every challenge and growth stage imaginable. No other leadership or team development consultant comes close to Annie's level and scope of experience. Her track record of success stems from her unique approach to business strategy, structure, systems, finance, and the "missing link" of behavior that brings it all together.

Whatever challenges you may be facing in your business, Annie has likely already seen it—and solved it. Some of Annie's current clients include fast-growing, high-level entrepreneurs like: Jeff Walker, Lisa Sasevich, Susan Peirce Thompson, Erico Rocha, Christian Mickelsen and Reid Tracy.

Annie holds a Bachelor of Arts, Phi Beta Kappa, Magna Cum Laude, from UCLA in Economics/Business, is a licensed CPA, and holds a Master's degree in Spiritual Psychology from the University of Santa Monica.

# About Leading Edge Teams

Leading Edge Teams has an unparalleled track record of helping businesses achieve massive, sustainable, TEAM-DRIVEN GROWTH...

What sets Leading Edge Teams apart is that, unlike any other company out there, our framework provides a COMPLETE, INTEGRATED SYSTEM for sustainable business growth and performance with each part working together seamlessly to fill every possible gap in your business.

**MINDSET**

(But not the "positive mindset" you're thinking of...) It's about shifting away from thinking you're the center of your business, to making your desired OUTCOMES the focal point. This shifts your responsibility to creating the CONDITIONS and SUPPORT your TEAM needs to achieve them.

**STRUCTURE**

These are the structures, systems and processes that ORGANIZE how you think about and work within the business. These provide the foundational infrastructure that allows team members to focus on ACHIEV-

ING OUTCOMES instead of getting distracted by chaos and endless re-inventing of the wheel.

## BEHAVIOR—THE PEOPLE PART

All team members taking effective action towards outcomes is how you succeed—that's obvious. Yet our human personalities, emotions, preferences and habits often drive counterproductive behavior, especially within teams. We create the ongoing "behavioral habits" with your team that help your company achieve the "high performance culture" where everyone can be relied upon to take the most effective actions to achieve results, while also demonstrating leadership excellence.

**BUILD TEAMS—BANISH BURNOUT**
**www.LeadingEdgeTeams.com**

| **Annie Hyman Pratt** | **Barbara Schindler** | **Heather McGonigal** |
|---|---|---|
| CEO / Founder | COO / Executive Consultant and Coach | Program Director / Executive Coach |

# 'A+' Leader Development Program and Mastermind

The 'A+' Leader Development Program and Mastermind is a training program in which Annie and her team develops your key leaders to step up, take ownership of, and drive the operations of your business—helping you achieve your biggest goals.

Through this program your leaders learn to effectively lead and manage your team—taking the pressure of team development off of you, so that you can focus your energy on being an innovative visionary.

**LeadingEdgeTeams.com/a-plus-leader-program**

# Ways to Work with Leading Edge Teams

**Online Classes** that teach leaders and CEOs about infrastructure and foundational pieces needed to build your team and support the sustainable success of your business. In these comprehensive trainings we address key topics such as Effective Team Meetings, Functional Organizational Chart with Roles, Hiring and Keeping 'A' Players, Onboarding and Training 'A' Players and Agreements of Leadership.

**Executive Coaching** is about developing leadership skills and implementing proven business programs. With Executive Coaching, you get the support you need in the most customized way. In this one-on-one coaching, we look at what is happening in the moment and get great leverage to implement lasting change. The best systems and processes will fail without strong focus on leadership and team behaviors. This is what we're known for in our work with executives, companies, and teams.

**'A+' Leader Development Program and Mastermind** is a leadership development program that includes a 10-course curriculum with group coaching and a business leader mastermind, as well as individual one-on-one executive coaching to support the integration of the program's teachings. Our key programs include "Visionary Master Plan," which is our high level strategic planning approach and "Functional Organization Structure with Defined Roles". Other programs include: "Performance Management" and "Executive Team Meetings."

**Rapid Implementation Programs** are targeted private engagements that address specialized areas to quickly move the needle for specific outcomes. Our key programs include "Visionary Master Plan" which is our high level strategic planning approach and "Functional Organization Structure with Defined Roles." Other programs include "Performance Management" and "Executive Team Meetings."

**Customized Consulting Engagements** are a custom designed way to bring Annie Hyman Pratt and her executive coaching team into your company. Engagements are crafted for the specific focus needed to up level your team and business outcomes. Our private client engagements are longer term and incorporate the infrastructure, the team/people and the behavioral pieces, and the visionary piece. This high-end business consulting is usually for larger companies with more complex or advanced situations, which Leading Edge Teams addresses very specifically with a plan for rapid implementation.

# Other Journals in this Series

***Ahead of the Curve***
**Released July 2020**

# What Our Clients Say

***Matthew Bruce, Head Olympic Weightlifting Coach and Co-founder of BRUTE STRENGTH***

What makes Annie and the Leading Edge Team's program different is that it actually taught us from the human perspective—specifically how to treat people in business relationships. And that, to me, is even a bigger aspect that goes beyond the nuts and bolts; any experienced coach can teach the business nuts and bolts. But I've learned it's the working relationships that carry a business for the long term.

They've (the team and I) have improved tremendously. Before, I would say, I was a bit more aggressive—that may be the right term—but now every time an issue arises, I can hear Annie talking about compassion, and being compassionate when I talk to my team. I'm trying to see things I used to be unaware of (growing in awareness), as I refer back to the importance of self-leadership in my business.

***Adee Cazayoux, Founder and CEO of WAG***

Personally, working with Annie—man, where do I even start? I first met Annie in 2015. I knew nothing about business at the time. I knew I had something that was growing, worthwhile and a great opportunity. At the same time I didn't feel like I had the confidence to organize a team, to go towards a mutual vision that was outside myself.

I also felt like I was too personally attached to my business; like my business succeeding or failing personally reflected on me. Annie has completely transformed those things for me. The way the organization works behind the scenes is much more organized. We all know where we're heading. And the place we're heading has nothing to do with me personally. That behavior change (focus off myself) provides a huge level of safety and confidence for me, as well as giving my team the same. They don't have to work on impressing me, since the focus for all of us is to head towards the goal, which I think, helps us be more successful in many different ways in the business.

***Angelique Giron, Online Visibility and Marketing Strategist***

Oh yeah, first I learned from Annie how to slow down! I'm a super quick person and want to make everything go away or fix it right away. Now I recognize that if I slow down and allow myself to go into solution mode (using critical thinking and agreement with the team), it's much better. As I've slowed down and quit expecting everyone to catch up with me, dialogue and problem-solving has become collaborative. Now, we work together and find solutions together!